Navigating the Customer Contact Center in the 21st Century

A Technology and Management Guide

by William Durr

ADVANSTAR

COMMUNICATIONS

Cleveland, OH

Printed in the United States of America

10 9 8 7 6 5 4 3 2 1

ISBN 0-929870-57-3

Library of Congress Catalog Card Number 00-108592

Published by Advanstar Communications Inc.

Advanstar Communications is a worldwide business information company that publishes magazines, directories, and books, produces expositions and conferences, provides a wide range of marketing services, and maintains numerous Websites.

For additional information on any Advanstar product or for a complete catalog of published books, please write to: Advanstar Customer Service, 131 West 1st Street, Duluth, Minnesota, 55802 USA; or visit www.advanstar.com.

To purchase additional copies of *Navigating the Customer Contact Center in the 21st Century: A Technology and Management Guide*, please call 1-800-598-6008; outside the U.S. call 218-723-9180.
Price per copy is $31.95; call for quantity discounts.

Publisher/Product Manager: Danell M. Durica

Cover and Interior Design: Dave Crouch Graphics. Cleveland, Ohio

Table of Contents

Introduction and Acknowledgments

A book I wrote titled *Building a World Class Inbound Call Center* focused on the "call center," which at that time was a growing phenomenon in the United States and other western industrialized countries. While the book breezily discussed call center technologies, its major focus was on a management process that drove productivity and quality measurements at the individual agent level to ensure call center efficiency and effectiveness. That book has been well-received by the user community around the world for its plain language and highly actionable recommendations.

But change is the only real constant. Since then I have been repeatedly asked if I had any plans to write another book that would illuminate technologies as well as the first book had illuminated call center management practices.

Clearly, there is a lot to write about. Call centers are changing under the weight of multiple influences. One of the most significant influences is the rise of the Internet. The Internet (or World Wide Web) is thought to be one of a small number of transforming events in the history of the world. A transforming event alters life forever after its occurrence. Not only is call center technology changing as a result of the Internet, the very term used to describe these centers is changing, as well. While no consensus may ever exist, many people now refer to Internet-enabled call centers as "contact centers." The word "call" is too limiting. Contact centers are places where phone calls, faxes, e-mail messages and Web site support define the range of communication interactions with customers and prospects.

I set out to update the management practices discussed in my first book and more thoroughly explain the technology that has begun to transform the contact center. I have had the benefit of working for a variety of vendors in the industry, gaining valuable insights into different aspects of contact center technology. I have also had the benefit of meeting and working with scores of intelligent people in all areas of the industry, from users of technology to creators of technology.

Like my first book, it would be disingenuous to imply or suggest that every idea put forth in this book is mine alone. I seriously wonder if anything is ever the result of one person's effort and thought. I can't possibly list everyone who has helped educate or inform me. Special thanks to the following people: Dr. Kathryn Jackson, Dr. Gene Swystun, Jim Carrekar, Gordon MacPherson, Brad Cleveland, Wayne Andrews, Mike Maloney, Dan Gardner, Jake Chacko, Lorri Weston, Roger Sumner, Paul Anderson. Andrew Waite, David Hadobas, David Paddon in Australia, Ken Reid in the United Kingdom, Bill Seguin, Laird Williams, Craig Shambaugh, Bud Jordan, Elliot Green, Tom Aiello, Sheila McGee-Smith, Paul van Berkum and Ofer Matan.

I have tried to avoid my American cultural bias in writing this book but it's not easy. Pieces of this book have been written in England, South Africa, Australia, China and the exit row aisle seat on various American Airlines planes to more places than I ever thought I would visit. While my cultural bias clearly shows, it is apparent to me that contact centers are the same around the world. We all worry about the same things. The only real difference I have noticed is that outside of the United States, contact center people tend to think that they are behind the technology curve. They believe that the art and science of contact centers is well advanced in the United States beyond their own implementations. It ain't so. Once upon a time it was true. But another result of the Internet is that ideas and technologies move with the speed of light. Ideas and products emerging in the United States in the morning are available around the world by lunchtime.

When I finished my first book, I never imagined that I would write another. Having completed this book, I am equally certain that I won't author another one on contact centers. But I am endlessly fascinated by the people, the processes and the technologies from which contact centers are fashioned. Give me a call. I'd love to hear from you. Dial (817) 488-3430. And remember: Your call is important, please stay on the line and your call will be answered in the order it is received.

Chapter 1:
Call Centers, Contact Centers or Convenience Centers?

Historical Perspectives

I find that many people have little regard for history. That's a shame because history provides a useful context or lens through which we can more appropriately view and understand current and near-term future events. Many people tend to feel that the pace of change is accelerating as we begin the 21st century. They don't realize that similar transforming events have impacted society and business before—in the 19th century, for example.

Consider a brief list of just some American inventions designed (mostly) in the last frantic 25 years of the 19th century: the passenger elevator, escalator, telephone, phonograph, air brake, cash register, electric light, fountain pen, linotype, box camera, pneumatic tire, adding machine, revolving door, safety pin, paper clip and typewriter. All were designed to relieve people of some everyday inconvenience. I'll venture to say that most of the inventive genius in the world across all of time has been directed towards making life more convenient for humans.

Certainly the telephone turned out to be a transforming event in human history. The ability to communicate instantly, across vast distances changed society, business enterprise and human dynamics. But before the telephone could be invented, there was an earlier transforming event that, for a time, seemed to be the be-all, end-all solution to human communication needs—the telegraph. After all, before the invention of the telegraph, communication across distance was accomplished by written documents. The pace of information exchange via correspondence was initially measured in months, then weeks and, finally, days. But the telegraph was the first communication technology that conquered distance.

A historical Royal Shaft award most certainly must be given to Professor Joseph Henry of Princeton, who in 1831 invented the telegraph. Joseph Henry? What about Samuel Morse? As it turns out, the good Professor Henry possessed a peculiar personality. He liked to look into things but seldom saw them through. Henry not only had the idea of transmitting messages as coded electrical impulses via wires, he worked out all the essentials that would be necessary to make such a system feasible. For some reason, though, he never bothered to perfect or patent the process.

Which brings us to Samuel Morse. Even if he never had been credited with the invention of the telegraph, he would still have been recognized as a man of distinction. He was an accomplished artist, a member of Britain's Royal Academy, a professor of fine arts at New York University, a dedicated dabbler in the creative sciences, and a would-be politician. His consuming passion, however, was the idea of transmitting messages along wires. In 1842, he persuaded Congress to fund his experiments to the tune of $30,000. It is an interesting historical sidelight that the governmental legislation funding Morse's experiment also provided equal funding for the study of mesmerism, more commonly referred to as hypnotism! Morse used the money to string a wire between Washington, D.C. and Baltimore and in 1844, he sent the first telegraphic message. Morse's only real invention was the simple code that bears his name. To build a working telegraph, Morse not only stole lavishly from Henry's original papers, but when stuck with a problem would call on the scientist for guidance.

Today, it is almost impossible to conceive how the telegraph astonished and captivated the world. Imagine, news from remote places available instantaneously, everywhere. For the first time in history, distance began to be conquered. It was, in its way, as astonishing then as the announcement of practical teleportation of humans would be to us today (Beam me up, Scotty!). Within four years of the first public demonstration, the United States had 5,000 miles of telegraph wire.

So, It's Communication You Want?

In 1876 an invention even more useful and lasting, and far more ingenious than the telegraph—the telephone—was invented by Alexander Graham Bell. Bell did not coin the term "telephone." The word had been around since the 1830s, and had been applied to a number of devices designed to produce noise, from a kind of musical instrument to a particularly insistent foghorn. Bell described his appliance on the patent application as a new kind of "telegraphy," and soon afterward began referring to it as an "electrical speaking telephone." Others commonly referred to it in its early days as a "speaking telegraph."

Bell had become interested in the possibility of long-distance speech through his work with the deaf. Like the telegraph, scholars now realize that Bell used the work of others and there is some controversy about exactly who should get the credit for the telephone's invention. Bell and his assistant, Thomas Watson, made that historic first call on March 10, 1876.

They quickly demonstrated their invention to Western Union, but the executives there failed to see the technology's potential. They referred to the telephone as a novelty and an electrical toy. Others were not so shortsighted. Within four years of its invention, the United States had 60,000 telephones. In the next twenty years that figure would swell to more than six million. The speed with which the telephone insinuated itself into American life is indicated by the fact that by the early 1880s when a person said "I'll call you," it was meant by telephone.

Here We Go Again

Apart from being mildly interesting, some people would dismiss the above stroll through history with a shrug. So what! But I see a delicious symmetry between that sequence of events and what is happening today with the Internet. The first useful application associated with the Internet communication protocol was e-mail, a written form of communication that has a time lag between initiating message and reply. This neatly parallels the use of written correspondence as the first communication method to challenge distance in ordinary human endeavors and business interactions. With the adoption of Web sites and the associated requirement to provide Web site support, the first practical Web page support technology is text chat. I regard text chat in much the same way as telegraphy. Both technologies eliminate the time lag between initiating message and reply. Both are hand oriented. One gets better (faster) with practice. And, they are both nonsimultaneous communication protocols. First I go, then you go, and so on, back and forth. As bandwidth improves and quality of service issues are resolved within the Internet protocol, the preferred technology for Web site support will be Voice over Internet Protocol (VoIP). There is an obvious correlation to the telephone that Bell invented all those years ago. The final symmetry is the eerie parallel between the reaction of Western Union executives to the telephone and many existing telephone company executives to the Internet as a fad or merely an electronic toy.

Customer Contact Space

It was nearly 100 years after the invention of the telephone that the first modern call centers were created. By that time the telephone was firmly established throughout the world as the primary communication tool. In western, industrialized countries people grew more and more accustomed to interacting with businesses by telephone. At first, consumer contact with business by telephone was personal. One rang a company and encountered an attendant or operator. The operator, typically a woman, greeted the caller, determined the nature of the call and extended the caller to the right person in the firm. As the volume of telephone calls into businesses increased, the number of operators required to handle the calls increased. It was noticed that the operators frequently had trouble locating qualified people to handle the transaction. The concept of automatic call distribution (ACD) was born. Because of limitations in then-existing technologies, primitive call centers were centralized. As technologies improved, call centers could be decentralized, using the telephone network to link multiple sites together. With the rise of the Internet and the introduction of multimedia communication modes, I began to envision the call center industry as a three dimensional space. Consider the diagram below:

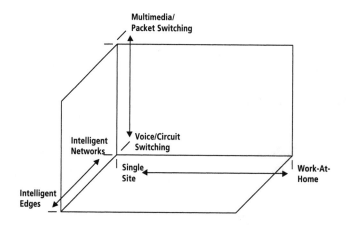

Figure 1-1. Customer Contact Space

Imagine a room diagrammed with the front wall, right-side wall and ceiling removed. In the beginning, all call centers were located in the corner, at the floor. This point in call center space is identified as voice/circuit switched, single site and reliant upon intelligent communication networks provided by the likes of AT&T and British Tel.

For more than twenty years, technology in call centers has moved along a single axis, along the "floor" and towards the right. From a single-site orientation, call center technology permitted the establishment of multiple sites. Thus, the notion of virtual call centers came into being. A virtual call center is one where multiple sites operate as if they are a single entity. As the cost of voice communication declined and the technology improved, the possibility of single agents working at home—yet still part of a single call center operation—emerged. It seemed that we had reached the endpoint of development.

And then the Internet impacted business and society. What had been a relatively simple environment was transformed into a three-dimensional space. Call centers began morphing into customer contact centers (figure 1-1) as multimedia communication modes emerged. The Intelligent Networks, discussed in Chapter 3, which were designed to handle voice and struggled to handle data began to yield to so-called dumb networks—fiberoptic networks. With fiberoptic networks, all the intelligence exists at endpoints in the form of routers and servers.

As I envision this contact center space, we are moving up and out from that corner on the floor. Implementations by leading-edge firms increasingly include experiments and pilots that bring in multimedia transactions and use of dumb networks. In my view, the industry has not moved as far as some vendors and trade press would have us believe. But we recognize that they have an axe to grind and profits to generate on behalf of their shareholders. I also recognize that not all firms are moving in the same direction. Some companies are still decentralizing their call centers while others are centralizing. Some companies are embracing multimedia and dumb networks; others are very content to sit on the sidelines and wait for more reliable, more affordable solutions to emerge. Moreover, it is very important to realize that the vast majority of call centers in the United States and around the world are still struggling to effectively manage voice operations.

Appropriate Technology

I suppose the biggest issue I have with some vendors and the trade press is the constant drumbeat that spells out the message that if your company is not fully engaged in voice over IP, Web site support, customer relationship management coupled with front- and back-office integration—you're on the way to extinction. This is a deceiving message on several fronts. In the following pages the case is made that all contact centers are not alike and extinction is reserved for companies that ignore people and processes as well.

Really question industry analysts on the subject and they will ultimately admit that plain old voice calling through the public-switched voice network will remain the dominant and preferred method of customer interaction for a long, long time. Yes, it's true that the Internet is bringing about significant change. A growing number of e-mail messages will likely end up being processed by call centers. But voice remains king.

We need to understand the proper role of technology. I think in terms of "appropriate technology." Rather than view the call center user community as a single market, it seems more sensible to consider it to be three related, but discrete markets. We might map these markets as depicted:

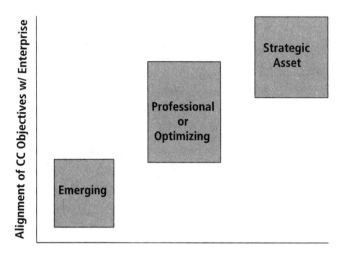

Figure 1-2. Market Segments

The three market segments are labeled Emerging, Professional (or Optimizing) and Strategic Asset. I first thought that these segments might be a simple function of the professionalism of the call center management team versus the length of time the center had been in operation, which roughly equates to size of the center. But I had trouble with that formula because I encountered smaller call centers that were strategic assets to their firms and saw lots of larger, well-established call centers that were seemingly stuck in the professional market segment forever. Gradually, it occurred to me that a better formulation of market segmentation results from assessing the strength of the Information Technology (IT) organization and its capabilities coupled with how well the goals of the call center align with the overall goals of the enterprise. That is to say: If the company has a strong, capable IT department and the goals of the call center mesh with the goals of the firm, then it is more likely that the call center will be at least Professional and quite likely that it will become a Strategic Asset.

Emerging Call Centers

Emerging call centers are generally smaller in size. If you were to ask the senior managers in the company if they had a call center, they would likely answer in the negative. Emerging call centers have basic needs in terms of technology and process. Their needs include the ability to:
  • handle, route and complete calls effectively;
  • improve agent telephone functions;
  • provide even call distribution;

- provide flexible answering options;
- provide recorded announcements to callers on hold; and
- keep pace with calling demand.

In general, emerging call centers usually have other tests to perform, in addition to answering incoming calls. This other work sometimes includes handling written correspondence, filing and record keeping. It is somewhat ironic that emerging call centers have to make do with fairly rudimentary technology that constrains informed, intelligent call center management practices. Smaller call centers are much more difficult to run while delivering consistent good service. The reason why smaller centers are more difficult to run successfully has to do with the pooling principle. Larger agent populations are inherently more efficient and more forgiving.

Professional Call Centers

I use the term "professional" in its broadest context. I don't mean to suggest that emerging call centers don't have professional management teams. The notion I am trying to emphasize is that if you were to ask senior management if the firm has a call center, they would emphatically agree that it does. The goals of a professional call center management team are straightforward and include the following:
- Reduce caller wait time
- Decrease transaction time
- Improve quality of customer interaction
- Improve agent productivity
- Reduce operating costs
- Increase revenue

I suggest that most call centers reach the Professional segment. They are formalized call centers, recognized throughout the firm. Their budgets become more significant as the number of agents increase. Because labor is the largest cost element in a call center's budget, senior management is always keen to keep operational costs under control. The perennial refrain is to do more with less. Thus, Professional call centers are usually interested in technologies and management practices that promise cost reduction and/or revenue enhancement.

Strategic Asset Call Centers

The final market segment is the Strategic Asset segment. Call centers in this market segment are very different from the previous two segments. Strategic Asset centers imply that it is hard to imagine the company being successful without a successful call center operation. Examples include the call center operations at Federal Express and American Airlines. Handling telephone calls is not the central purpose of either firm. Moving packages and flying passengers are the essential purposes of those companies. Yet, it is hard to imagine that either could be successful without the call center component. In fact, the very success of these firms is directly tied to the successful operation of the call centers.

Strategic asset call centers are different in many ways from the other two ·market segments. Consider their needs:
- Create new revenue opportunities
- Expand applications, create new involvements
- Support new ways of doing business
- Provide useful insights and information to other departments
- Become a unique, sustainable competitive difference

Nowhere in this list do you find edicts to reduce transaction time or improve productivity. This does not mean that Strategic Asset call centers don't worry about those metrics. They do. But operational metrics are not their exclusive focus. They are intimately connected with the overall business purpose that is their main focus. If spending more time with each caller promotes loyalty and raises revenue and profits, that is more important than the labor budget expenditures that an increased headcount incurs.

People, Process and Technology

Call center technology needs change as the expectations and requirements around the center change. Some vendors still strongly suggest that what it takes to run a center successfully is simply their technology. Many people see it differently. There is appropriate technology for every call center. What is important to achieving call center operational success is a combination of three elements: people, process and technology.

People are the most important asset. It is when a skilled agent interacts with a prospective customer and is supported by the right technology and management processes that the magic happens. Things get sold. Problems get identified as a first step towards resolution. Loyalty increases. These are the magic things we want from our call center operations after all is said and done.

Process is the next most important thing. I mean this in two different senses. The call center management team must have its own management processes in place, well-defined and clearly understood by everyone in the center. The management team also needs to have business processes clearly defined and understood by everyone in the center and everyone that the center interacts with in the extended enterprise.

Technology is the last consideration. When processes are in place and staff is trained and motivated, focus upon the technology. Too little technology or the wrong kind of functionality results in people working much too hard. You notice that the agents' cubicles are papered over with yellow sticky notes filled with exceptions and reminders. Too much technology or functionality ahead of need or purpose results in budget nightmares. Senior management believes that you have all the best tools. So, you had better produce. Training requests and motivational necessities will go out the window.

It is a difficult balancing act to maintain. Keeping the proper proportions between people, process and technology requires skill and hard work. It is among the goals of this book to bring the reader some perspective on two of the three basic elements: Technology and Management Process.

Chapter 2:
The Changing Role
of Call Centers

Call Centers—Origins

The first modern call center was created as a joint venture between what is now Rockwell Electronic Commerce and Continental Airlines in 1973. In the intervening years, call centers have undergone significant technological change and have been integrated into nearly every industry in all industrialized countries around the world. Call centers are generally defined as a place where callers can quickly and efficiently conduct transactions with trained, skilled company representatives or obtain needed information from automated sources.

Businesses have embraced call centers for a variety of reasons. In the beginning, call centers were used almost exclusively to generate revenue. In this context, it's not surprising that airlines were the first to use call centers. They were interested in selling airplane seats, a highly perishable commodity, as efficiently as possible. After the door shuts, the empty seat represents a cost burden. Therefore, it was sensible to make it very easy for people to get through to airline agents to purchase seats.

In the past decade, call centers have taken on a bigger role in the delivery of customer service. Business executives in many industries began to recognize that competitive differences were difficult to sustain. If product differences were difficult or impossible to create, progressive firms discovered that a competitive advantage could be gained by making it very simple for customers to conduct business transactions with them. Call centers, and the applications they serve, are being established in ever-increasing numbers and existing centers are being expanded in size and scope because they play a central role in the acquisition of new customers and the retention of existing customers. And they accomplish these missions in a cost-effective manner.

The Evolution of Call Centers

Call centers are fascinating places because they are unique combinations of technology and people. While there are lots of places in an enterprise with lots of people or lots of technology, the call center is unmatched in terms of mixing these two volatile ingredients together. For historical reasons we refer to the people as "agents" (the airline origins still exert influence) although customer service representative (CSRs) and telephone service representative (TSRs) are generic terms gaining currency. The technology utilized in a call center consists of a bewildering collection of technologies with imposing acronyms like ACD, IVR, CTI and LAN. We should count ourselves lucky that there are only 26 letters in our alphabet or the acronym jungle might become impenetrable. We will review the technology in the chapters that follow. For now, let's appreciate why call centers keep changing and understand the major forces that are shaping the transformation of voice-oriented call centers into 21st century customer contact systems.

Call center components and capabilities keep changing in lock step with changes occurring in networking, information systems, the general competitive environment and the predilections of the sea of humanity that they serve.

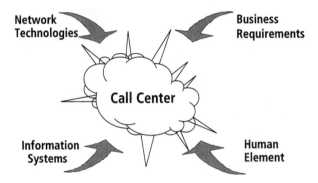

Figure 2-1. Convergence of Influences on the Contact Center

We can argue about which element has exerted the greatest influence. The best that can be said is that the rank order of influences shifts over time.

Early on, changes in the telephone network caused call centers to change. As the globe's telephone networks changed from purely analog to digital and later to ISDN (Integrated Services Digital Network), call centers changed to take advantage of new services. A good example is DNIS (Dialed Number Identification Service), which gave call center users the much-appreciated ability to handle any transaction type on any physical 800 (free calling) circuit. Prior to DNIS, call center users had to provision a discrete set of circuits for each call type. Put more simply, the call center had a group of circuits for the sales application and a different set of circuits for the customer service application. For example, callers dialed 1-800-555-1000 for sales and 1-800-555-1100 for customer service. Years ago in the United States, 800 circuits were priced in two ways: (1) a relatively expensive flat monthly fee with unlimited usage, or (2) a very small monthly fee coupled with per-minute usage costs. As a consequence, users spent time worrying whether they had too many or too few circuits. Too many circuits imposed unnecessary costs and too few circuits meant that callers could not get through. DNIS changed all that. Users could combine the circuits into one, more efficient, group. The last four digits that the caller actually dialed were transmitted to the call center equipment. Through these digits, the call center technology could determine what kind of transaction type was being presented. This apparently simple change in telephone network technology caused tremendous change in call center equipment. The ACD (Automatic Call Distributor) had to be re-engineered in a variety of ways, affecting trunk interface cards, call processing software and real-time and historical reporting software. The general trend of call center technology has been to move from a relatively rigid, predefined set of processes towards more free-form, make your own rules process environment.

Continuing the theme more recently, call centers have begun to change in response to the stunning societal impacts coming out of the Internet and wireless industries. Much more will be said about those influences in a later chapter.

Call centers have also changed in response to changes in information systems. A useful insight into call center technologies can be obtained by examining the changes in information system technology. Business data processing in the early 1970s was totally reliant upon mainframe computers. Mainframe computers were large, proprietary systems with limited access, primarily through so-called dumb terminals. These dumb terminals had no local intelligence whatsoever. Shortly after mainframe computers gained preeminence, the first generation of ACD systems appeared in the marketplace. The first generation of call center systems looked a lot like mainframe computers from an architectural viewpoint, not altogether an amazing coincidence.

From the mid-1970s through the present, we have witnessed an amazing transformation of the computing landscape with echoes into the call center industry. First, mini-computers were developed. They were physically smaller but still powerful computers that supported clusters of dumb terminals. Moreover, mini-computers were really good at communicating with each other. It was the need for speed in data communications that really began to alter the technological landscape.

Modem technology of that era permitted speeds up to a generous 9,600 bits per second, turtle-speed by today's standards. As a result,

Local Area Network (LAN) technologies began to emerge, first Ethernet and then Token Ring. The concept of file servers was born. Personal computers began to emerge. Wide Area Networking (WAN) technology was developed.

These changes impacted call center technology in several ways. As general-purpose computers became less expensive and more powerful, ACD systems became more affordable and less rigid. Lower cost computing systems permitted the development of voice mail and Interactive Voice Response (IVR) systems, important ancillary devices in call centers. Voice mail and IVR together with DNIS, discussed earlier, caused ACDs to change in response. ACD systems had to become user-programmable. The response from the vendors was to provide user-accessible database and routing tables (also known as call vectors or call control tables). These routing tables permitted users to gain limited control over ACD resources like agent groups, announcements, and music sources.

Voice mail's utility was incorporated into the call center as an agent group of last resort. The art of managing a call center lies in balancing a dynamic call load against a limited agent population. This infers that some callers will wait. Call centers employ various strategies to induce the caller to wait, such as delay announcements and music on hold. Voice mail seemed to be an excellent alternative for callers who had waited too long. For this reason, some vendors decided to incorporate voice mail subsystems directly into their ACD systems so it could be integrated into call center operations.

Interactive Voice Response (IVR) systems emerged as the first nonhuman answer resources. Essentially, these systems permitted a telephone user to query computer databases via the telephone touch-tone pad for answers to straightforward questions such as:
• What is the balance of my account?
• When will my order ship?
• Where can I find a dealer?

A very simple form of IVR became known as an Auto Attendant. This application permitted organizations to offer single-number service into the call center and then give the caller a menu of transaction choices from which to select.

In the face of these changes in environment, ACD systems became more powerful. Not only did they deliver the functionality of first-generation ACD systems, now they had to interface and interact with these additional elements.

The other two significant prevailing influences, Business Requirements and the Human Element have arguably even greater impact upon call center evolution than do changes in communications and information processing.

Businesses find themselves in hotly competitive times. Communications and mass media permit firms to extend their served markets to global proportions. Companies were local and measured their effective operating territories in miles in the 1800s. Now, all firms can become global by establishing a virtual presence via a Web site. If the product or service is compelling, people around the planet will find them and do business. The communications revolution has fostered truly global marketplaces.

Somewhat blunting the explosive growth in business reach is the shift in power to the consumer. Apart from specific needs, we observe that citizens of industrialized, consumer economies around the world share a number of issues. High on anyone's list is time starvation. The things that we must do intrude further and further into the fixed 24 hours in each of our days. Workdays are expanding. Chores must be done. Tasks and obligations abound. As a result, consumers demand convenience. And they demand it from every company they do business with, for every product or service they consume. If they don't get convenience, they punish those companies by doing less business with them than they might have. Or, they decide to do business with another company altogether.

The business and social landscape continues to change by virtue of several influences:
- Explosion in computer power
- Dramatic decrease in computer costs
- Standards in the computer industry
- Adoption of local and wide area networks
- The Internet and multimedia transactions.

These changes in environment can be thought of as the democratization of computing. Powerful yet inexpensive computers are available to both workers and citizens. Standards have fostered interoperability among diverse computing elements. Information moves freely at high speed within and between sites on local area and wide area networks. As computers have gained in power, the applications and development tools have likewise progressed to allow even more powerful and robust applications to be considered and implemented.

The powerful forces identified above are altering call centers in fundamental ways. We can argue that all the changes that took place to this point were a linear form of evolution much like that embodied in Darwinian evolutionary theory. Charles Darwin postulated that evolution was a process of small changes over very long periods of time, a very gradual process. Meanwhile, Moore's Law, named after a visionary at Intel, holds that computer power doubles every 12 to 18 months or that the same computer power declines in price by half in the same time frame. The Internet garnered 30 million users in less than 5 years, the fastest uptake of any technology ever witnessed. These startling, sudden and sweeping changes suggest to many that today the evolution of call centers is better characterized by a competing evolutionary theory first advanced by the famous paleontologist Stephen Jay Gould. Gould described an evolutionary process that was characterized by swift, sudden changes interspersed by long periods of linear change. An example of this evolutionary theory is that what killed the dinosaurs was the impact of a huge asteroid upon the earth that very suddenly changed the global environment. Gould's evolution is nonlinear, discontinuous and features an inflection point—an event that is significantly transforming.

Up to this point, call center technology had changed by accretion. Elements and functionality were added in steps and layers. Generations of technology formed. Reflect for a moment on how ACDs have changed over the generations. In the beginning, ACD systems were totally proprietary and self-contained. They scanned trunk and agent ports for state changes in real time. They processed calls according to the user rules. They generated operations information and delivered it in real time to supervisor screens and printed historical reports. Just as the Balkans region of Europe splintered into ethnic nations as we approached the millennium, the ACD has undergone some splintering of its own. What we are seeing is the gradual transformation by deconstruction of a telephone call processing system into something much more—a multimedia, multi-format customer transaction processing center.

The World Wide Web/Internet's impact on the call center is just beginning to be felt. The Web has already undergone several generations of evolution. Sites have moved from essentially passive brochures to online interactive experiences, and most recently to channels for commerce. More studies have been conducted in this area. Jupiter Communications, in a 1999 study, reported that online shopping revenue is expected to grow to $41.1 billion by 2002. The last Christmas buying season demonstrated that Web sites that had no provision for real-time customer service were far less successful in generating revenues through the site. Studies have shown that fully 90% of online customers prefer human interaction. And nearly 50% of online shoppers visit multiple sites before making a purchase. A recent Yankelovich study revealed that 63% of online shoppers said they did not finish a transaction because they could not find the information they needed.

Online shopping is not the only Web interaction that firms have to be concerned about. Many consumers have already purchased your product or service and are using your Web site for customer service, support and assistance. Your ability to provide a satisfying experience for these customers is key to long-term retention and growth. Satisfied customers tend to buy more and tell others about their experiences, creating the positive "buzz" that every company hopes to generate in their marketplace. So, the next phase of e-commerce evolution must involve the venerable call center because even with the Web and the Internet, we come back to customer service. Increasing numbers of businesses globally have embraced customer service as a key to gaining and keeping the competitive advantage. Business management consultants like Tom Peters have spread the gospel of customer service far and wide. An article in the *Harvard Business Review* entitled, "Putting the Service Profit Chain to Work" and "The Loyalty Effect," which appeared in the *Harvard School Press*, attempted to quantify the differing impacts of poor and good service. These articles suggested that:

- Nearly 70% of all customer defections are a result of poor customer service.
- It is five time more costly to acquire than to retain customers.
- On average, U.S. firms will lose 50% of their customers in five years.
- Service leaders on average grow twice as fast as service laggards.
- Service leaders enjoy improved market shares.
- Service leaders are able to charge as much as 10% more for their goods and services.
- Increasing customer loyalty by 5% can increase profitability by 25 to 85%.

We can debate how to precisely define what customer service is. At a detail level, customer service is a collection of tasks and processes that varies from industry to industry.

Our perspective is that customer service can be defined at a high conceptual level as *making it easy for customers to do business with you and developing a corporate memory*. Notice that customers still seem to prefer doing business by telephone. The major difference these days is that the phone is increasingly wireless. We have more to say about the impact of wireless technologies in a later chapter. For now, recognize that the rest of the world is far ahead of the United States in terms of wireless telephone use. There are many reasons for this. The United States still is working out which of various competing transmission standards will prevail. The rest of the world seems to have settled on GSM (Global System for Mobile Communications). It is estimated that nearly a half billion people use mobile phones. More that half of all those handsets adhere to the GSM standard. Moreover, in the rest of the world wireless phone users do not pay to receive calls as they do in the United States, which is why mobile phone use is so prevalent in everyday life by ordinary people internationally.

The global love affair with the telephone has never been more evident. Phones are everywhere. They are convenient. They are immediate. Everybody knows how to use one. Everybody has basic verbal skills. Phones are very personal communication tools. And, they are interactive. When you compare this list of advantages to any other method of communication, such as mailing letters, exchanging data via computer or using messenger services, it is easy to understand why the phone is preferred. As popular as e-mail has become, if telephones took as long as personal computers to boot up, we might all still be using Morse code.

The Mission of Customer Contact Centers

The mission of call centers goes beyond revenue generation or the delivery of customer service. Admittedly, these two processes are important and companies ignore them at their peril. The real mission of customer contact centers is to help the enterprise understand and react to our rapidly changing world.

It is widely reported that time no longer moves at the familiar pace. The concept of "Internet time" is akin to so-called "dog years" and holds that a calendar year equates to seven years of Internet time. Things change that fast. The pace of business and life has accelerated tremendously. Patience is a lost virtue. Some people refuse to wait in even relatively short telephone queues. Instead, they fire off an e-mail message. Travel to a nearby retail shop? No way! Many people prefer to log on to the Internet and virtually shop where there are no crowds, no hassles finding a parking space, and more choice than most can rationally deal with.

Since customers and prospective customers are likely to contact a business through any of a number of means, the call center is being transformed into the multimedia contact center depicted below.

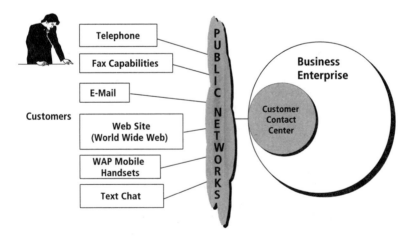

Figure 2-2. Multimedia Contact Center

Make no mistake, voice communications will be a dominant feature of contact centers for a long time. But the Internet and related electronic communications are already having a profound effect on contact center technologies and operational challenges.

The depiction of the multimedia contact center as the focal point between the world and the enterprise is intentional. A 21st century contact center is a communication node for the enterprise or company. It touches all communication, and information flows into and out of the company. Its specialty is real-time communications like voice telephone calls, voice over IP (Internet Protocol) as part of Web-page support and Web-page support scheduled callback requests. Because agents have developed keen senses regarding etiquette and call control, as well as proficiency in policy/procedure and product/service knowledge, they are uniquely skilled to handle other forms of interactions given the proper training and development time.

This picture fits neatly into the focus on internal streamlining that preoccupies so many companies. Time is recognized as the most precious of commodities. We discussed time starvation among consumers earlier. Time is also a serious concern for companies. As the world speeds up, firms see that their internal pace needs to speed up as well. For more than one hundred years, the organization model has featured departments. The sales department. The accounting department. The shipping department. And so on. Even inside good firms, these departments operated more like fiefdoms. They were mostly concerned with what was going on inside the department. Linkages to other departments were ad hoc and incidental.

In the 21st century, firms are spending time and money to break down the silos within them. The information technology infrastructure available makes the vision of a seamless enterprise attainable. Back-office operations such as inventory, billing, accounts receivable, just-in-time manufacturing processes and so on can and should be linked to so-called front-office operations or customer-facing environments embodied by call centers, marketing, sales forces and virtual Web sites. Because so many people now have so many choices by virtue of our Internet-connected world, consumer loyalty is at an all-time low. We covered the time-value of a typical customer earlier. If loyalty disappears entirely, how will firms retain customers over time?

It is not going to be enough to simply make it easy for customers to do business with you. Companies need to develop a corporate memory about each individual customer. Psychologists generally agree that human memory has two distinct components; a short-term memory mechanism and a long-term memory mechanism. For example, when we obtain a telephone number from a directory we use short-term memory to retain it until we dial the number. That piece of information doesn't get transferred to long-term memory and the next day, or in my case the very next minute, we can't recall it at all. In the 21st century contact center, your customers will be engaging you through a variety of communication channels. They will expect you to link these different communications together and remember them so that with the next contact all previous contacts and their content are available to the agent. Moreover, it will be necessary that the agent understands what kind of products and services have been purchased by the customer in the past. With a corporate memory, firms can begin to implement one-to-one marketing as described and popularized by the globally popular consulting team, Peppers and Rodgers. It is generally agreed that the more a company knows and remembers about each customer, the higher the customer retention rate will be. Going forward, enterprises will increasingly find that customer retention will be the key metric for success—and even survival.

Chapter 3:
The Networks Around Us

"May you live in interesting times" is a Chinese curse. "Interesting times" in this context is usually a euphemism for upheaval. We are witnessing an upheaval of epic proportions as the very fabric of our communication network undergoes a startling transformation. A former Federal Communications Commission director once said that what we have is a voice network struggling to handle data while what we are moving towards is a data network that can handle voice. It is useful to have a high-level working knowledge of both kinds of networks and, in fact, these two competing networks form one of the basic dimensions of the contact center space referred to in the first chapter.

Circuit-Switched Voice Network

The existing voice telephone network has been under construction for more than 100 years and by any measure has been extraordinarily successful in its mission of providing reliable voice connectivity between people across vast distances. In more technical terms, we refer to the voice network as a circuit-switched, intelligent network. These terms have clear and important meanings.

Nearly everyone understands that the voice network is digital. But it is not digital in the same way that computers are digital. It is important to understand the difference.

Human voice is analog. Our voices are the complex interaction of air moving across vocal cords modulated by the positioning of our tongues, teeth and lips. The result, viewed on an oscilloscope, is a complex waveform. The early telephone systems transmitted this analog waveform as it was, without transformation. While technologically easy, analog transmissions proved susceptible to noise and interference from outside, transient signals produced by lightening and radio waves. In the late 1970s and early 1980s, the telephone systems around the world began to migrate toward digital transmission in an effort to avoid noise and interference.

Digital Voice

Early on, various vendors proposed proprietary digitizing schemes. Among the earliest was a linear digital encoding scheme implemented by a company called Rolm, whose claim to fame was their creation of the first digital Private Branch Exchange (PBX). The beauty and elegance of digitizing voice lies in the promise that voice and data could be treated exactly the same. Moreover, once digitized, voice transmission was immune to noise and interference stemming from stray electromagnetic sources such as radio stations, home appliances and natural phenomena like lightning.

Rolm and other vendors began to envision a future where voice and data moved to the desktop along a single connection. In fact, a number of firms shared this vision during the early 1980s. A turf battle of sorts developed between PBX vendors and enterprise data network vendors over which technology would prevail. Companies such as Rolm, Datapoint and Intecom offered essentially telephone switches as erstwhile hubs of the so-called electronic office.

Central to their product offerings was the digitization of voice. The analog waveform emerging from our lips was transformed into ones and zeros. The standard that resulted is known as Time Division Multiplexed, Companded Mu-Law encoding. In plain language, the analog waveform is sampled 8,000 times per second. An eight-bit value is assigned to represent the instantaneous value of the sampled waveform. The result is a stream of bits, 64,000 bits per second, which encodes the analog voice waveform very faithfully and yields excellent audio fidelity. All modern telephony adheres to this basic standard.

Intelligent Services Digital Network (ISDN) technology is the result of separating the encoded digital voice streams from the data signals that facilitate switching and billing concerns. ISDN circuits come in two flavors; Basic Rate Interface (BRI) and Primary Rate Interface (PRI). Basic Rate Interface circuits provide the user with two Bearer (B) channels and one data (D) channel and is referred to as 2B+D. The bandwidth allocation is two 64,000-bits-per-second channels and one 16,000-bits-per-second data channel for signaling. The Primary Rate Interface circuit is more commonly known in the United States as a T-1 span line. It consists of 24 Bearer channels and one data channel. In Europe and other areas of the world, a variation on Primary Rate Interface exists that has 32 Bearer channels and one data channel. It is called an E-1 circuit.

Not all telephone companies have the ability to use the D channel to send signaling information. In cases where the D channel can't be used, that information is instead delivered over the B channels. In this instance, each B channel in a Basic Rate Interface circuit can only send and receive data at 56,000 bits per second because the other 8,000 bits per second in each channel is used for signaling information. When the B channels carry signaling information, the process is referred to as "out-of-band signaling." When the D channel carries signaling information, it is referred to as "in-band signaling."

At one time, many believed that PBXs would be the mechanism that brought about the convergence of voice and data. PBXs, it was thought, would merge the bit streams of computers together with digitized voice and vastly simplify the infrastructure. It was not to be. Computers spoke a myriad of "languages" called protocols. Computer vendors created unique protocols in an attempt to lock users into a particular brand. While human languages could be easily digitized, nobody realized that it would take much more time and effort to create a unifying language for computers. We will explore that in just a few more pages.

The Intelligent Digital Voice Network

The voice network is called an intelligent network because the "smarts" reside in powerful Central Office switching equipment. Your home phone is serviced by what is known as a Class 5 Central Office, more commonly known as the local exchange. For example, I live in Grapevine, Texas. There are about 30,000 people who live here with me. We are served by a Central Office that supports a part of Grapevine through two exchange numbers; 488 and 481. Each of these exchanges can support 9,999 distinct telephone numbers (488-0000 to 488-9999). When I call my neighbor down the street to complain about his dog digging in my yard, the Grapevine Central Office is smart enough to know that both numbers are under its control. It arranges a connection from my phone to the Central Office and back out to my neighbor's phone. This connection is full-duplex, meaning that we can simultaneously shout at each other about the dog's behavior. A good analogy for this connection is to imagine that the Central Office built a two-lane highway between my phone and the neighbor's phone. Our conversation is the only thing traveling on that highway. Even when we are both silent, mulling over our next words, the highway remains ours alone until we hang up. From a resource usage standpoint, it is very inefficient.

But what happens when I place a call to someone outside of the 488 or 481 exchanges? The local exchange only knows about itself. When presented with a connection request beyond its own boundaries, the exchange sends out a data message to a nearby Class 4 Central Office, which can be viewed as an exchange of exchanges. Instead of supporting telephone sets, a Class 4 Central Office supports a number of local exchanges. In fact, the entire network is comprised of a hierarchy of Central Offices. Each has its own view and span of control over the switching world. Sitting atop everything are special facilities called Service Control Points or sometimes Signaling Control Points (SCPs) which are fast, complex computers handling data messages from Central Offices. These data messages can be viewed as queries from the requesting Central Office as to where and how to make connections as requested by the calling party.

For quite some time all the major InterExchange Carriers (IXCs) such as AT&T, WorldCom, British Tel, Telstra and Sprint have literally operated two networks; the voice network we all know and a data network called Signaling System 7. For call center users, the free calling services represented by "800" numbers in the United States are a special case. After all, "800" numbers are essentially fictitious telephone numbers. More appropriately, "800" numbers are merely billing mechanisms behind which exist real telephone numbers. We can depict the modern telephone network with respect to 800 calling as follows:

Figure 3-1. The 800 Network

When a caller, represented in the drawing as the handset near Florida, calls our 800 number, the call moves from the local exchange to the nearest Class 4 Central Office Point of Presence (POP) for the InterExchange Carrier that controls that 800 number. The voice portion of that call gets parked at the POP while a data message is sent to the InterExchange Carrier's Service Control Point (SCP). The SCP is a complex database that uses the number that was dialed and the number placing the call to determine what real telephone number the call attempt should be routed to.

Once the SCP has determined what real telephone number to route the call to, a return data message is sent to the Class 4 POP. Now the Class 4 Central Office "knows" where to send the call.

All voice circuit-switched telephone networks work in a similar fashion around the world. It is evident why we refer to these networks as intelligent: The smarts are embedded in the Central Offices and the data networks that coordinate the interoperation of thousands of such Central Offices. At the end-points of the circuit-switched voice network are rather stupid devices that we know as telephones. Without the complex switching intelligence behind them, telephones are similar to paperweights—they take up space and do nothing.

The circuit-switched voice network is a marvelous creation. For all its complexity, it is easily the most reliable technology we possess. Of all the essential modern services such as electricity, natural gas and water, the voice telephone network is almost always available. It is simply not possible to make similar statements about the other essential services.

Because each conversation on the voice network represents a dedicated two-lane highway, voice network engineering practices are built on the premise that not all telephone users wish to use the network at the exact same moment and that voice conversations typically are measured in minutes and then end. These assumptions turn out to be key. In fact, we have seen firsthand what happens when everyone wants to place a call at the same time. Central Offices cannot respond fast enough to all the simultaneous service requests. The result is that some callers don't receive a dial tone. For callers that do receive a dial tone, there are a fixed number of paths out of the local exchange Central Office. When those paths are fully occupied by other callers, your call attempt receives a fast busy signal. A fast busy signal differs from the more familiar busy signal we hear when the number dialed is already engaged in that the cadence of the busy tone is faster. Fast busy signals are the result of too few paths out of the local Central Office, too few paths between hierarchical Central Offices, or too few paths into the local Central Office that supports the called telephone number.

Events that stimulate large populations to place telephone calls at the same time occur regularly. National holidays are the best and easiest example. Natural disasters also trigger mass telephone calling. But problems associated with the second key assumption—voice calls are typically measured in minutes—turn out to be the source of the upheaval in the network fabric.

The Rise of Data Connections

Over the years, more and more data is communicated between computer systems. Everyone knows that computers represent everything in ones and zeros, as bit streams. The voice network was built to handle human voice, an analog stream. So, modems were invented that transform the computer's bit stream of ones and zeros into a "voice". If you've ever listened in on a data transmission between two computers, you hear a tone carrier wave that is modulated by the stream of ones and zeros. To our ear it sounds as if the tone carrier wave is warbling and quavering. Even with sophisticated statistical tricks, the conversion of data from ones and zeros to something that the voice telephone network can deal with limits the speed of data transmissions. That is problem one. The greater problem, insofar as the voice telephone network is concerned, is that data "calls" last a long time. Compared to ordinary voice conversations, data conversations go on seemingly forever. In fact, when U.S.-based Internet Service Providers (ISPs) uniformly changed their billing from usage-based to flat monthly fees telephone companies around the country raised a huge fuss. With longer data conversations, they saw a real and growing need to expand their networking facilities without receiving very much incremental revenue in return, until they realized that households would need second and third telephone lines to accommodate their growing communication needs.

The amount of data being transmitted continues to grow. And the need for speed continues to increase. Luckily for us, another network was already under construction. This network would be very different from the intelligent voice network. This network would be oriented around ones and zeros from the very beginning. It would enable computers to talk to each other in a single, uniform protocol. It would carry digitized voice, as well. It would be the mechanism that really enabled the convergence of voice and data. And we would come to know it as the Internet.

Packet-Switched Networks

The Internet is a packet-switched network. Its origins go back to the late 1960s. The U.S. Department of Defense was interested in funding experiments with communication systems that could withstand damage. This was the Cold War era and communication was a central element of command and control systems being studied by the various branches of the armed forces. Communication networks with centralized intelligence are highly vulnerable to bombs and nuclear weapons. The Advanced Research Project Agency of the U.S. Department of Defense built an experimental computer network called ARPAnet. ARPAnet connected military researchers and universities, allowing them to share computer resources. The network also allowed communications between and among the connected users via e-mail. The network's chief characteristic was that it was totally decentralized. There was no central intelligence. In practice, this meant that if parts of the network were destroyed, the rest of the network continued to function by ignoring the damaged portion and going around it.

ARPAnet grew and adapted to emerging technological developments, notably mini- and micro-computers. Some large organizations constructed private networks that used the basic ARPAnet protocol and hooked directly into the ARPAnet, as well. Congress had funded the U.S. National Science Foundation (NSF) in the 1980s to create five supercomputer centers to be used and shared primarily by universities. The NSF's traffic began to explode in volume, especially after it expanded the availability of its network beyond university researchers in computer sciences, government workers and researchers. The NSF decided that anyone in a university and even commercial organizations and individuals would be permitted to hook into its network. In 1987, the NSF contracted a private company to work with IBM and MCI to upgrade the network. And, they changed its name from NSFNET to the Internet.

To a casual observer, the Internet seems like nothing else. Who owns it? Who runs it? Who pays for it? The answers are nobody and everybody. Governmental agencies, universities, telephone companies and large private firms all build and operate special networks called backbones, which are very high-capacity lines carrying enormous amounts of Internet traffic. These lines are usually fiberoptic cables. The capacity to move ones and zeros on a fiberoptic line is tremendous. It's not just a function of having thousands of individual glass fibers in a small bundle. Each individual glass fiber strand transmits data at the speed of light. White light is actually composed of all the colors of the rainbow, each color having its own wavelength. These days, each wavelength of light can carry its own data stream (this is called Dense Wavelength Division Multiplexing or DWDM). Thus, within a single strand of glass fiber many, many high-speed independent transmissions are taking place. Therefore, placing a single fiberoptic cable bundle into the ground between two points represents a lot of transmission capacity. It is not surprising that companies, universities and agencies have spare capacity to sell. And sell it they do, to regional and local Internet Service Providers (ISPs) that provide Internet connectivity to individuals and firms. The fees that we pay to our ISP help to pay for the Internet. All these organizations belong to a loose association that agrees to broad rules and procedures established by advisory and governing boards. Among the more important of these governing bodies is the Internet Registry, which records the connections between addresses and administers domain names (part of an Internet address).

How the Internet Works

A seemingly simple set of ideas makes it possible for computers and networks to share information and messages on the Internet: Break up all information and messages into pieces called packets, deliver those packets to the proper destinations, and then reassemble the packets into their original form after they've been delivered so the receiving computer can view and use them. That's the job of the two most important communications protocols on the Internet. Transmission Control Protocol

(TCP) breaks down and reassembles the packets. Internet Protocol (IP) is responsible for making sure the packets are sent to the right destination.

Unlike our voice telephone network, in a packet-switched network there is no single, unbroken connection between sender and receiver. Instead, when information is sent, it is broken into small packets, transmitted over many different routes simultaneously, and then reassembled at the receiving end.

Instead of hierarchical Central Offices, the Internet is built from various transmission facilities such as telephone lines, T-1 span lines, satellite circuits and fiberoptic cable bundles. The hardware that supports the Internet consists of hubs, bridges, gateways, repeaters and routers. Hubs are important because they link groups of computers to one another. Bridges link local area networks (LANs) with one another. They allow data destined for another LAN to be sent there, while at the same time keeping local data inside its own network—in your building or on your floor, for example. Gateways are similar to bridges, but they also translate data from one kind of network protocol to another. An example of this is a gateway that connects an Ethernet LAN to a Token-Ring LAN.

When data travels across the Internet, significant distances can be involved. These distances present problems in that the signal weakens across the miles. Repeaters amplify the data at appropriate points in the network to overcome this problem.

But the key role in Internet traffic flow is played by routers. Their job is to make sure the packets always arrive at the proper destination. When you initiate an e-mail message to someone at another company across the country, routers examine the packet's destination address and take into consideration the amount of activity on the various Internet paths available to it at that moment. Their main task is to move each packet to another router that is closer to the packet's final destination. Notice that the packet is moved to a router closer to the destination and not directly to the destination. That is the power and elegance of the Internet. There is no central intelligence that knows where everything is. Instead the Internet can be thought of as hundreds of thousands of routers, each of which has some knowledge of the routers closest to itself. Should a particular router fail or should a fiberoptic bundle that connects to some other router be severed, the sending router learns that that particular path is no longer functional and stops using it in favor of other, still-functional routers and fiber bundles.

A little insight into the packet itself helps to flesh out our understanding of the Internet. For various reasons, some esoteric, an Internet packet contains about 1,500 characters. Each packet is given a header that contains a variety of information, including the order in which the packets should be reassembled and the maximum number of hops that the packet can experience. The router also calculates a checksum that is a number derived from the actual number of ones and zeros contained in that packet. The checksum figure is used at the receiving end to determine whether any errors were introduced into the packet during transmission.

Each packet is put into separate IP envelopes that contain addressing information. All of the envelopes for a given message or file have the same addressing information so they can all be sent to the same location. As the packets are sent across the Internet, routers along the way examine the IP envelopes and look at their addresses. The routers determine the most efficient path for sending each packet to the next router closest to the final destination. After traveling through a series of routers, the packets arrive. Because traffic load on the Internet changes constantly, the packets might be sent along different routes and they might arrive out of order.

As the packets arrive at their destination, TCP calculates a checksum for each packet. It then compares this checksum with the checksum that has been sent in the packet. If the checksums don't match, TCP knows that the data has been corrupted. It then discards that packet and asks that the original packet be retransmitted. When all the noncorrupted packets are received by the computer to which the information is being sent, TCP assembles them into their original, unified form.

Packet networks are desirable because they are resource efficient. Recall that the voice telephone network figuratively builds a two-lane highway between callers. Even when nothing is being said, the connection and all the resources utilized to maintain that connection are engaged and cannot be used by others. In a packet network, highways are shared by millions of individual packets with much greater efficiency.

Also notice that the devices at the edges of these two networks are very different. Because the voice telephone network is intelligent, the telephone instrument itself is essentially dumb. Because the Internet network is dumb, having no intelligence within it, the devices at the edges are intelligent. We call them personal computers. However, we already see that personal computers are giving way to so-called intelligent appliances that are some-thing like a computer but less imposing for the user. Which brings us to the third network changing our lives, the wireless network.

Mobility

Cellular telephony has been around for many years. It has gone through evolutions similar to voice networks, moving from analog to digital transmission. Like computer systems, there are a number of competing protocols that make it impossible for a cellular telephone to operate everywhere on the planet. But we are getting close. Outside of the United States most of the world's cellular providers have settled on a protocol known as GSM. It is not my intention to discuss how wireless networks operate, since in a large sense they are not fundamentally different from the voice telephone network. At a very basic level, wireless networks employ radio to connect the mobile user into the network. Once the mobile caller has reached the closest antenna, the call is virtually handled the same as any other telephone call.

Because people are time starved and demanding of convenience, mobile phones have moved beyond being symbols of status and are becoming the Swiss Army knife of the 21st century. Some cellular phones are equipped with powerful computer chips embedded within them and employ a data transmission protocol called Wireless Application Protocol (WAP). Some look like an ordinary cellular phone, except they have a lengthwise hinge that allows them to open up like a clamshell. Inside is a much larger screen than is normally associated with a cellular phone and a small keyboard. A WAP cellular telephone is a marriage between a telephone and a computer. The user can engage in mobile telephone conversations on one hand and access the Internet on the other hand. Some WAP cellular phones also offer speakerphone capabilities, address book functionality and appointment/calendar systems.

The WAP technology was invented because the complex, interactive graphics provided by many Web sites are incapable of being properly displayed or viewed on the relatively small displays found in cellular phones. What mobility users want is useful information, not fancy, eye-catching graphics. WAP technology notifies people via e-mail about events and situations that are important to them. They can view information that has relevance and meaning to them. Because mobile phone providers know where the mobile phone user is located moment by moment, geo-graphically appropriate information can be conveyed to the user. And based on the e-mails and information displays, they can place a phone call. All from the same small device while they are on the move or disconnected from home or office.

We begin to perceive how the networks and devices we have built can simplify and enrich our lives. For example, I am in a meeting in another city. During the meeting my cellular phone receives an e-mail message sent by the airline that I am scheduled to travel home on later that day. The e-mail message informs me that my scheduled flight is going to be delayed into the city where my meeting is taking place by bad weather at its origination and asks if I want to consider alternative flights so that I can get home in time to watch my child perform in a school concert. I place a phone call to the airline to book a different flight. The process is unobtrusive, convenient and immensely pleasing. Without these tech-nologies, such an occurrence is simply impossible. How would the airline find me? How would I learn that my scheduled flight will be late? How would I explain to my child why I missed that magic moment?

Three Networks, One Aim

We live in a changing world where three very different communication networks are growing in scope and functionality. There already exists in the United States millions of miles of fiberoptic cable. A good portion of that capacity is "dark," as in unlit or unused. Several other companies have announced intentions to build out fiber networks totaling more than 15 million more miles in the United States alone.

Meanwhile, traditional telephone companies around the world are forming alliances, strategic partnerships and colossal mergers. They see a much bigger market—a global market—providing individual callers with neat, timesaving features and global reach, anytime and anywhere.

And, the mobile telephone industry is undergoing consolidation of its own so that free-ranging services are more easily provided as service offerings begin to explode with the impetus provided by WAP mobile phone capabilities. Third-world countries view mobile phone networks as a means to leap into the 21st century. They don't have the time or resources to build an inground, copper communications network. Cellular telephone networks can be built relatively quickly compared to traditional copper networks.

Three very different networks undergoing growth, experiencing prodigious change in technologies and struggling to provide the same thing in the end—convenience.

Why All This Bandwidth?

It has been calculated that the capacity of the fiberoptic networks already in place is equal to the capacity of the copper-based telephone networks in the United States combined. And still more fiberoptic cable networks are planned to come online over the next few years. A reasonable person might ask: How many phone calls and data flows do we expect need occur? The answer is—a lot. More than we can imagine because communication might become nearly free.

Already, we have seen long-distance rates plummet. The General Services Administration (GSA), a kind of purchasing agent for the U.S. federal government, has entered into a long-term agreement with Worldcom and Sprint. Any agency of the government, without regard to communications volume, can obtain long-distance service under this agreement. Rates for long-distance start at just under $.05 per minute in the first year of the agreement and are scheduled by contract to shrink to under $.01 per minute by 2004. If you believe, as I do, that the two InterExchange carriers supplying service to GSA still plan to make money in 2004, then you begin to realize what is happening to transmission costs as the aggregate amount of bandwidth explodes.

Distance has been a persistent problem for humans since the time when oral and written communication were first established. After thousands of years, we are on the verge of conquering distance. Distance will not matter. In a world where transmission costs approach zero, everyone will enjoy virtual telepresence.

Chapter 4:
Contact Centers:
A Technology Road Map

Contact centers are neither created instantaneously nor of whole cloth. They evolve in the same way as living organisms. They change slowly over long periods of time. Then, because of some sudden change in the environment or because of the influence from some significant transforming event, the rate of change or the evolutionary path is altered in dramatic ways. This chapter will discuss the various technologies employed in contact centers. Along the way we will review the following:

- Automatic Call Distributors
- Interactive Voice Response
- Voice Mail
- Workforce Management Software
- Quality Monitoring Systems
- Computer Telephony Integration
- Virtual Contact Centers
- E-Mail Management Systems
- Web Site Support Mechanisms
- Desktop Workflow Systems

There is no specific or more correct sequence in which these technologies should find their way into your contact center.

ACD System Architecture Simplified

At the heart of any contact center is some kind of voice-switching system. These switching machines have a variety of names. Key systems, Private Branch Exchanges (PBXs), Standalone Automatic Call Distributor (ACD) systems and Central Office (Centrex) systems can all serve as competent voice-switching platforms upon which contact centers can be constructed. The function of the switching engine is to connect a calling party with an employee who can handle the caller's transaction. Nearly every kind of

switching engine has some ACD capability. ACDs are different than UCD (uniform call distributors) and call sequencers. An ACD:
- provides for distribution of workload by routing calls to agents according to user-defined rules;
- manages incoming call traffic by employing a queuing or waiting list assignment to each call;
- provides management information reports on system and agent performance;
- provides real-time monitoring of workload.

The callers arrive at the switching vehicle via telephone circuits. Typically, these circuits are either local trunks or "800" circuits. Physically, there is little difference between the two. The difference lies in who pays for the call. "800" service is one of the fastest-growing segments of the telecommunications industry. The calling party bears no expense for calls directed toward "800" numbers; the business enterprise publishing the "800" number bears the costs of all calls. Obviously, the callers prefer to deal with companies that publish "800" numbers.

The different kinds of ACD systems used in contact centers are similar in function. The following diagram illustrates the pertinent functions and elements of switching systems:

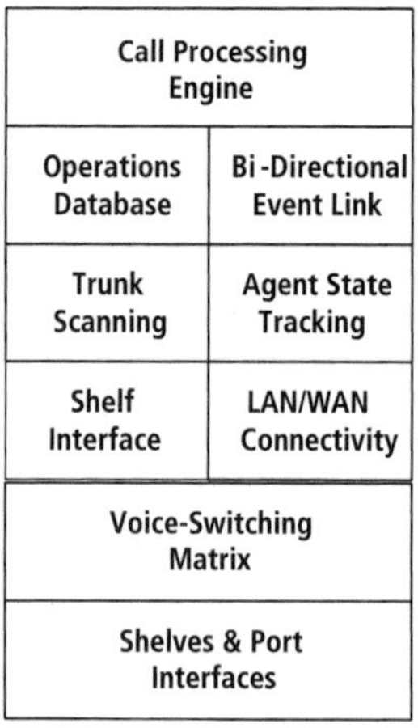

Call Processing Engine	
Operations Database	Bi-Directional Event Link
Trunk Scanning	Agent State Tracking
Shelf Interface	LAN/WAN Connectivity
Voice-Switching Matrix	
Shelves & Port Interfaces	

Figure 4-1. Typical Switching System

Although modern switches do not really connect a trunk with a station user in the same sense that electromechanical switches did, the metaphor is useful. The actual switching fabric these days consists of time slot interchange accomplished via solid-state memory. However, this technology is so like magic that thinking in terms of physical switching is easier.

Trunks are terminated into circuit cards within the switch. The ACD common control manages a process that scans the trunks for changes in state. For trunks, there are usually two states of any importance; on-hook and off-hook. The switching system knows from the trunk type definition what to expect when a trunk goes off-hook. Either a caller is literally coming down the wire or digits are going to arrive. More on that in the section on call routing.

When a switching system notices that a trunk has gone off-hook, it looks to its call processing rules to determine what the user wants done with the caller. Call processing is covered more thoroughly later. It might be necessary for the switch to connect the trunk with one or more internal devices such as digit receivers, announcements and music-on-hold sources before finally connecting to an agent.

While the trunk is being processed (milliseconds actually), the ACD common control is scanning the ports associated with stations. Specifically, those stations that are defined as call distribution agents are monitored for changes in state. For agents, there are a number of possible states as follows:

Available—the agent is ready to take a call

ACD In-Call—the agent is already engaged in a call

Wrap-up or After-Call Work—the agent is doing work related to the last call handled

Idle or Unavailable—the agent is present but not ready to take calls

Internal—the agent is talking with another station user inside the company

Outcall—the agent is talking on an agent-initiated call external to the company

When the ACD common control finds an agent in the available state, it checks the database to determine if that agent is qualified to handle the caller. The system "knows" the general nature of the caller's transaction by virtue of the trunk the call arrived upon, by digits the caller dialed before connection to the switch or after connection via replies to prompts. If the available agent is qualified to handle the caller, the ACD links the trunk with that agent's station line and the conversation commences.

It is typical for a contact center to operate with queues. The ACD keeps a list of call arrivals in the order received. There might be call processing rules in effect that alter the pure "first in, first out" queue removal process. In slack calling periods, the ACD can also keep a list of available agents. In this fashion, the ACD ensures that agents receive roughly the same amount of work during the day. At the heart of all contact centers is the rule that says the *longest waiting caller* will get connected to the *longest available agent*. In actuality, a busy contact center will connect the longest waiting caller to the *next available* agent, while a lightly loaded contact center will connect the *next caller* to the longest available agent.

Perhaps one of the best metaphors for modern contact centers is the old switchboard attendant.

Figure 4-2. Early Version of Call Distribution Technology

Consider the old-style switchboard where an attendant sat in front of an imposing array of long cords with massive brass plugs and orderly rows and columns of jacks. The attendant would answer incoming calls with a greeting and ask a few questions to determine what the caller wanted to accomplish. Then the attendant would find a station user and make the physical connection between caller and station user. What we find in this imagery is the perfect contact center analogy. The attendant is performing the functions of the ACD common control with respect to scanning the ports. Then the attendant performs the physical switching. We can stretch the analogy by recognizing that the attendant of old was the source of much information about who was calling whom and how many times they had spoken that day. The attendant was fulfilling the MIS function so important in the modern silicon implementation of today.

ACD Architecture Evolution—First Generation

More than 25 years ago, the first generation of ACD systems appeared in the marketplace. Back then, most large companies relied on mainframe computers for data processing. Many business units within these large companies did not have direct access to data processing resources. Telephone systems were stark by today's standards, with few features and fewer options. If a business unit could justify computer access at all, it was achieved through the use of dumb terminals with low-speed connections to the mainframe.

First-generation ACD systems were required to provide a self-contained solution. That is, not only were they expected to perform the voice switching, but they also were expected to:

- drive supervisor displays in near real time;
- control many agent instruments in real time;
- produce hourly, daily and historical printed reports.

Given the state of computer technology, vendors achieved this functionality by using totally proprietary designs. And, because computer power was relatively limited, the call processing flexibility afforded the user was likewise limited. Calls were processed using physical trunk routing techniques, discussed a few pages later in this chapter. Agents were organized into simple agent groups. There was no notion of agent skill groups. There was the concept of primary and secondary agent groups that provided for a very crude call overflow capability. Reporting was limited. Real-time supervisor screens were predefined and unchangeable. Printed reports were of a fixed format and contained limited data elements.

ACD Architecture Evolution—Second Generation

During the early 1980s, the environment changed in significant ways. Computer power increased. Personal computers began to emerge. The long-distance network gained intelligence. Intelligent subsystems, like Dialed Number Identification Service and Interactive Voice Response (IVR), began to impact telephone operations. These technological changes caused ACDs to change in response. ACD systems had to become much more user-programmable. The response from the vendors was to provide routing tables (also known as call vectors or call control tables). These routing tables permitted users to gain control over ACD resources like agent groups, announcements, and music sources.

In the face of these changes in environment, ACD systems became more powerful. Not only did they deliver the functionality of first-generation ACD systems, but now they had to interface and interact with these additional elements. Second-generation ACD systems are characterized by call control tables or call vectors, integrated, proprietary voice mail subsystems, and standard interfaces to external IVR systems. Reporting demands placed on the system and increased call processing demands resulted in a division and specialization in function, with outboard minicomputers being used to deliver management information. This was the beginning of the deconstruction of ACD systems. Up to this point, ACD systems were evolving by addition. Previously separate subsystems were being added to ACD systems much like Microsoft kept adding previously separate software functions to the Windows® operating system.

ACD Evolution—Next Generation

In the beginning, ACD systems were totally proprietary and self-contained. In the second generation, more and more previously discrete subsystems were integrated directly into ACD systems. But as user requirements in reporting grew, self-contained operations databases and rigid report designs became far too limiting. Vendors realized that no matter how much time and effort they spent on designing reports and providing new data elements—they were wrong in the eyes of the next potential customer. The solution, and the entire theme of next-generation evolution, was to be found in deconstruction rather than accretion.

The first change had to do with the ACD database. Instead of being internal and closed, next-generation ACD systems provide for a standard database provisioned on a local area network (LAN) server. While the vendor provides data retrieval tools as part of the product offering, the user is free to use existing Information Systems tools such as Crystal Reports™, PowerBuilder™, Visual Basic™ and even Excel™.

The next component to splinter off the ACD and on to the increasingly ubiquitous local area network/wide area network (LAN/WAN) computing environment is the agent telephone instrument. Most fully featured ACD systems have a proprietary agent telephone instrument. They typically have large special function keys and displays to simplify and speed the mechanics of handling calls. Many of the leading vendors have introduced software applications that eliminate the physical telephone instrument. The software places a phone panel or toolbar on the PC screen, while the agent's application runs as normal. When the phone panel software is TAPI compliant (Telephone Application Program Interface, a standard promoted by Microsoft for integrating PCs and telephone operations), interesting first-party computer telephony integration (CTI) applications can be developed inexpensively and quickly.

A third emerging change involves control over call processing itself. When first introduced, ACD call processing commands were relatively crude and simplistic. Later, call processing was improved with the concepts of conditional commands. More recently, call processing practices were again improved with the concepts often referred to as skill-based routing. More about these subjects will be discussed later.

The common element found in this progression of capability is that the ACD is always referencing itself. Outbound telemarketing and database routing require a different approach. In outbound telemarketing campaigns, specialized software outside the ACD takes control of the switching and call processing logic and tells the ACD what to do step by step, including what numbers to dial; at what pace; and, which agent gets connected to a live answer. In database routing, leading-edge companies have decided to process callers in relation to the value of that customer to the firm. (Note: This practice predates the overhyped concept of Customer Relationship Management by many years.) Good customers get good service. Average customers get average service. The value of a customer to a firm is likely to be in enterprise databases, not capable of being summarized inside an ACD routing table. So, third-party software is being created that works in lock step with ACD systems. The caller's identity is determined by the ACD. That identity is sent to the third-party database routing software module. That module determines the value of the caller and assembles a history of the relationship. The module tells the ACD what to do with this particular caller and coordinates the delivery of the screens to the agent eventually connected with the caller. What we see unfolding is the disassociation of the switch control processes from the switching engine itself. As we shall see, this deconstruction seems necessary so that the routing and reporting functions perfected over 25 years in the voice world can be applied, where appropriate, to the multimedia world.

Future Architectures

A very useful concept has largely been corrupted by marketing hypemeisters. The term "open system architecture" was coined to differentiate new, emerging system architectures from older, more proprietary architectures. We have seen in an earlier chapter that the first call center systems were entirely proprietary and closed. There was no other choice if users demanded and vendors desired to offer systems that featured very high reliability.

With second and successive generations of technology, systems became less proprietary and slightly more open. Although vendors began referring to their systems as "open," a better description would have been "semi-proprietary." "Open" as a descriptive term for contact center technology seems to have *devolved* in meaning to equate with "runs on a Windows platform" and/or has an event and message link so that other applications can take control of the switching engine. There are a few advantages associated with that, but they tend to benefit the vendor more than the buyer/user. Developing software for Windows environments is easier simply because of the vast number of tools and deep pool of programming talent.

So, what we see in the market are several different variations of "semi-proprietary" designs. Traditional ACD vendors have the operational database on a server. Some have the call processing running over a Windows operating system, usually NT. Many have well-defined message and event links so that third-party software can interact with the switching system. Other vendors, the so-called "all-in-one" vendors like Interactive Intelligence and Apropos, build a complete telecommunications system on a Win-Tel platform that provides for enterprise telephony, call distribution, voice response, multimedia integration and unified messaging.

I refer to all of these as semiproprietary because the true characteristics of a "really open system" are simple and straightforward. Number one, I can buy the physical parts of the solution from a variety of sources, which helps ensure low prices. This refers to servers, trunk interface cards and agent/telephone station interface cards. If the vendor requires you to purchase any or all of these items from them and them alone, it is a semi-proprietary device. Number two, I can add or substitute software applications from other sources easily. Instead of being forced to use an IVR application that the vendor has built into the system, if I wish to make use of another vendor's IVR application, that is permitted and is easy to accomplish.

A New Architectural Paradigm

It has been suggested repeatedly that the telecommunications industry closely parallels the information technology industry in a trailing manner. That is to say, the IT industry experiences something first, then much later the same thing begins to impact telecom. With the perspective that time brings, it is clear that standards and interoperability are the two key elements in securing optimal solutions affordably. This is demonstrated in the IT industry. The same concepts are emerging in customer contact technology.

The Enterprise Computer Telephony Forum (ECTF) consists of a long list of vendors spanning the entire range of traditional telephony and upstart Internet-related firms. Over the span of several years, they have created a set of specifications that might change the way contact center technology is developed and purchased. To frame the ECTF environment, it's useful to remember that, in most cases, contact centers deploy pieces of technology from different vendors. It is not unusual to find Vendor X's ACD working with Vendor Y's IVR. Soon we will commonly see contact centers mixing ACD, IVR, and e-mail management systems. There are real, incremental costs associated with putting together an ACD and an IVR, for example. These two devices are typically physically and programmatically linked as might be depicted below:

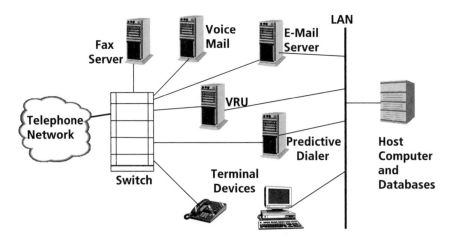

Figure 4-3. Traditional System Integration

For reporting reasons, most configurations would place the IVR system behind the ACD so that the IVR ports look like agents. This is a nice, elegant solution. It does cost the user incremental expense for the extra links between the ACD and IVR systems. The ports and interface cards and the software that runs them have real, calculable costs.

Beyond the so-called "plumbing" expense associated with integrating voice across systems, there are costs associated with multiple database administration, coping with change and successor training. But the biggest headache and expense is found in the integration expense associated with each piece of the puzzle. Each interconnection line represents both physical expense and integration expense. Moreover, a change in just one element might have repercussions across many other elements of the system.

The ECTF standards in this area are referred to as the S.100 Interoperability Agreement. I encourage you to visit their Web site at **http://www.ectf.org**. My generalized interpretation of what they are striving to achieve is to decouple the software applications from the voice, multimedia and Web interface devices. Dialogic, now part of Intel, provides a S.100 compliant platform via its CT Media offering. The advantage is that physical resources are shared by applications. Interoperability is the key word. Integration always implies effort. This is true whether the integration is done on-site, as is typically the case or before shipment like the "all-in-one" solution providers. I think interoperability means that the software model within which the application runs provides for well-defined edges, in a manner of speaking. Not only is the software environment concerned about vertical integration, it is concerned about horizontal integration.

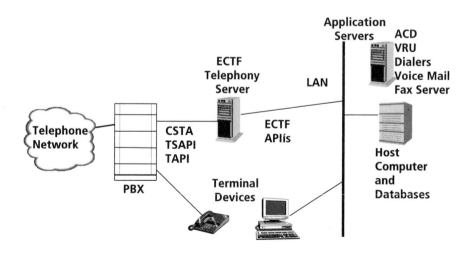

Figure 4-4. ECTF Software Model System Integration

In our case, the ACD is a software application and so is the IVR. The IVR application deals with the caller and, when needed, hands the caller over to the ACD application while informing the ACD application items of interest about the caller's interaction so far.

The point of the ECTF effort is to foster application development from a diverse source of vendors around the world. This will create an amazing array of choices for organizations, leading more rapidly to a high-functionality, high-return/lower-ownership-cost world. Users will truly reach this enviable position when they are able to treat applications such as transaction processing/routing, interactive voice response, real-time reporting and so on, as pluggable software modules running on any of a variety of servers.

Call Routing

Call routing consists of the rules that a user establishes to sort callers by transaction type, priority, calling source, identity or other useful criteria. Over the years, call distributors have become more and more powerful in their call routing capabilities. While any division of these capabilities into categories is arbitrary, the following general classifications are useful:
- Physical Trunk Routing
- Digits Received Routing
- Rules-Based Routing
- Skill-Based Routing

Physical Trunk Routing

As the name implies, this routing capability is basic functionality in ACD equipment. When a call center has more than one kind of transaction and the skill set required by those transactions is too difficult for every agent to handle every kind of call, the need for specialization among the agents emerges. This creates a problem. How to get callers to the right group of agents?

Basic systems use a physical trunk routing mechanism. That is, the business publishes two different telephone numbers ("800" or local). The caller has the responsibility to discover the correct telephone number to dial. As described earlier, when the ACD sees a circuit go off-hook, it looks into its database to determine which agent group is responsible for that kind of call. If the agents are all busy, the system plays a message and places the callers into queue. The system continues to scan for an available agent. Most systems permit the user to overflow a caller who has been waiting too long to an agent in another group. This presumes that the agent in the other group is sufficiently trained and equipped to complete that caller's transaction.

There are problems with physical trunk routing. The biggest problem is that the callers are responsible for dialing the right telephone number. Frequently, they dialed the wrong telephone number. The initial agent would have had to transfer the caller to the correct agent group. This led to the next problem—the management information became more complex and difficult to understand. As the number of internally routed calls increases, the more difficult it becomes to understand what is happening as a first step towards improvement. In addition, dedicated trunk groups are inherently less efficient and require more attention to ensure that the company is fully meeting caller demand. It still sometimes happens that a growing call center finds itself undertrunked with respect to total demand. If you have too few connections to the Central Office, callers will be blocked in the Central Office or in the network before the call attempt is logged into your system's MIS.

Digits Received Routing

As call centers grow, better call routing mechanisms are required. Direct Inward Dialing (DID) has been around for many years. Inter-Exchange Carriers offer a similar feature as an option to "800" service called Dialed Number Identification Service (DNIS). This neat feature provides trunk economies of scale. Whenever you manage to consolidate smaller groups into a larger group, you will find a rewarding economy of scale. If you initially have 5 trunk groups of 6 circuits each, you might discover that a single trunk group of only 24 circuits provides the same call handling capacity.

With DNIS, the ACD system knows that when the circuit goes off-hook it must be prepared to receive a series of digits. Typically, the number of digits passed is four and these digits are usually the last four digits that the caller dialed. These digits are received by the ACD and compared with call processing rules that the user has created. The digit pattern in effect points to the rules to follow for that call.

Initially, the number of permissible digit patterns that a carrier would pass was equal to one less than the number of physical circuits in the "800" DNIS trunk group. For example, if you had 20 circuits in your "800" group you could publish and receive 19 different DNIS digit patterns. It wasn't long before some users began to see that they could use a unique DNIS digit pattern to identify the caller rather than the transaction type. The limiting factor was the number of permissible digit patterns. Some interexchange carriers accommodate their users by permitting them more permissible digit patterns than the actual number of trunks. Armed with this powerful feature, many users began to use DNIS to differentiate call processing not only by transaction type but also by who was doing the calling, at least at a group level. This was the first time that there was an efficient way to engage in relationship marketing in the call center. It still remains an effective way to segment your customer and caller population. After segmentation is accomplished, users quickly think of ways to provide different levels of service and different ranges of services for each level.

At minimum, DNIS is a useful tool to acquire some trunk economies of scale. After all, the major problem with having multiple numbers is that the responsibility is on the caller to choose or remember the right number. It is still there with DNIS.

Automatic Number Identification (ANI) is an option on "800" circuits that provides the complete calling telephone number. If a user's database is complete enough and good enough, ANI should permit the user organization to identify the caller before answering the call! This feature is much more powerful than DNIS because it relieves the caller from having to dial a special number. The user organization benefits by having a single "800" number to publicize. Of course, the largest benefit will be the enhanced relationship marketing that the contact center can engage in with this feature. There is more about the benefits and problems associated with ANI in the section about Computer Telephony Integration.

Rules-Based Routing

In recent years, all the leading ACD vendors have provided higher-level call processing features that are referred to as rules-based routing. Essentially, the user is handed a blank sheet of paper and is provided a command vocabulary. The vendor empowers the user to create their own, unique call processing rules within the confines of the command vocabulary, or call processing lexicon. Differences among switch vendors can be measured in tangible ways regarding the number of permitted routes, the number of permitted steps in a route, how quickly changes can be made in routes, how quickly the changes take effect, and the richness of the lexicon itself.

There is considerable debate about which vendor's lexicon is superior. To our knowledge, no vendor has implemented a call processing routing command lexicon exactly like the one created here for illustrative purposes. This imaginary, idealized command lexicon consists of the following:

Agent Group XX	Agent (ID, Position #)
Music Source X	Announcement XXX
If (condition), Then (process)	Hold XX Seconds
Go To Step XX	Go To Table XX
Disconnect	Answer
Voice Mail XXXX	IVR XXX
Dial (XX...X)	Query Site XX
Priority X	Send Busy
Collect Digits from Caller	Send Digits to Host
Receive Digits from Network	Receive Digits from Host

The reason why this kind of command lexicon is useful has to do with how its elements can be used together to create call processing rules and procedures. A basic call processing route might be portrayed as follows:

1. Agent Group 1
2. Hold 18 Seconds
3. Announcement 5
4. Music Source 2
5. Hold 45 Seconds
6. Announcement 10
7. Go To Step 5

In our lexicon, callers entering this routing table would be offered to any agent in Group 1. If an agent is immediately available, the caller will be immediately connected to that agent. If no agent is currently available, the caller will hear network ringing for 18 seconds. This is about 3 ring cycles. During the ringing and all subsequent steps, the call processing computer is always looking for an available agent in Group 1, and if it finds one it immediately connects the caller. After 18 seconds, the caller is connected to the announcement contained in location 5. This might be our first delay announcement or other appropriate initial message. Then the caller is connected to music source 2, which is playing an appropriate musical program. The caller will listen to this music for an additional 45 seconds before being connected to the contents of announcement location 10. The neat loop-back step is designed to cycle callers through an endless loop of announcement location 10 every 45 seconds until the caller is connected to an available agent in Group 1, or the caller abandons the attempt.

Examples illustrate the power of a command lexicon. Most agree that routing a call to a particular agent is an un-ACD thing to do. Yet, there are lots of applications where any agent can handle the first call from a customer but where follow-up calls from that customer need to be handled by a particular agent. This can be the case in the insurance claims industry, among others. The Agent (ID, Position #) command element would permit individual agents to be part of an agent group to handle initial calls and still permit follow-on callers to gain direct access to their case adjudicator.

One ticket-selling organization worried about music-on-hold. They could find no single music source that seemed to satisfy callers demanding tickets to events ranging from rock concerts to opera engagements. They felt a need for multiple music sources. If a user were to couple this kind of routing command with available services that mix promotional messages in a music context, they would have a powerful marketing-on-hold tool.

The most interesting call processing capabilities are created when users begin to use conditional commands. In our basic call processing route example, we could have substituted a conditional statement in place of the first command as shown:

1. If more than 10 callers in queue for Agent Group 1, then send busy
2. Agent Group 1
3. Hold 18 seconds
4. Announcement 5

This command relieves the contact center manager from having to continuously monitor conditions by predefining certain conditions and the actions to be taken when they occur. In our example, the contact center manager has decided that when there are ten callers already in queue for the agents in Group 1, the system should send busy signals to new callers until the queue is less than ten callers deep. The impact of this command element is directly related to how many and what kind of conditions the command structure includes. A set of useful conditions would include:

Time of day	Day of week/month/year
Percentage agents available	Number of agents available
Number of agents staffed	Message queue
Number of calls waiting	Age of oldest queued call
Average speed of answer	Service level goal

The usual implementation of this capability is that if the condition is met, the call processor will perform the action specified in the second part of the command. If the condition is not met, the call processor will move to the next step in the table.

The inclusions of commands for Voice Mail and IVR ports would make integration of existing devices easier in call processing applications. Many ACD systems have proprietary, well-integrated voice mail systems or have certified one or two voice mail vendors compatible. But many organizations already bought voice mail years ago and would like it to work with the contact center. In the insurance claim example previously cited, it would be advantageous to specify a voice mail port belonging to a particular agent. In this way, you could specify in self-documenting form the call coverages for individual agents engaged in repeated transactions with selected customers.

The Query Site and Dial Number commands would make running multisite contact centers much easier than it is today. Suppose our firm operates multiple contact centers. With our lexicon, the contact center manager would place a Query Site command after first attempting to handle calls at the incoming location. The Query Site command would literally ask other sites which among them was in the best position to take an overflow call. After identifying which of several sites could take an overflow call, the Dial Number command would use an ordinary dial-up circuit to overflow the caller towards the remote site.

The Collect Digits from Network or from Caller coupled with Send Digits to Host and Receive Digits from Host would self-document and make the switch to host link applications much simpler. These kinds of routing commands and the myriad paths that they generate provide the reason why a Go To Table command should exist. No vendor would ever likely provide enough steps in a single routing table to cover all potential applications.

An example of complex routing using some of the concepts in our ideal lexicon follows:

1. If calls waiting for Agent Group 11 > 12, then send busy.
2. Agent Group 11
3. Hold 18 seconds
4. If time of day > 1200, then play announcement 24 (Good afternoon...) or else play announcement 23 (Good morning...)
5. Hold 15 seconds
6. Agent Group 17
7. Play announcement 22 (Sorry for the delay...)
8. If time of day > 1600 or messages waiting for Agent Group 11 > 15, then go to Step 10 or else play announcement 14 (Apologize for delay, press 9 to leave message)
9. Collect one digit from caller; if "9" go to Step 15 or else go to Step 13
10. Play announcement 27 (Thank you for continuing to hold)
11. Queue 45 seconds
12. Go to step 10
13. Play announcement 30 (Sorry you're having difficulty...)
14. Go to step 10
15. Play announcement 15 (Key in phone number...)
16. Collect 7 digits from caller; if "timeout" go to Step 23
17. Play announcement 17 (The number you entered is...)
18. Play digits received
19. Play announcement 18 (If number correct press "1")
20. Collect 1 digit from caller; if "1" go to Step 21 or else go to step 15
21. Play announcement 19 (Leave message at tone)
22. End table
23. Play announcement 21 (Did not receive phone number)
24. Play announcement 10 (Please hold)
25. Raise priority to 6
26. Queue 999 seconds

The above complex routing table illustrates how custom call processing treatments can be created from a standard lexicon. In this example, the contact center manager has decided to reject new callers if the number of calls waiting for agent group 11 exceeds 12 calls. If the number of calls waiting is less than 12, then the caller is offered to any agent in group 11. If no agents are available the caller will hear central office ringing for 18 seconds as the user disguises the wait time and avoids In-Wats billing. The manager uses time of day testing to play the appropriate first delay announcement and then expands the search for an available agent to include agents in group 17. After holding for 30 seconds longer the manager has programmed the call processor to test for either 4:00 PM or the number of existing voice mail messages for group 11. If either condition is met, then the caller is placed into a loop which continues to play a periodic message until the caller is handled or abandons. If neither condition is met, the manager has established a message-taking routine that includes capturing the caller's phone number for automatic dialing. Attempting to duplicate this kind of call processing flexibility without an extensive command lexicon is simply not possible.

Call routing is at the very heart of the value added by ACD systems. Conditional routing (IF statements) is unquestionably the most important element of a routing lexicon. The ability to examine the current condition of the various elements of the center (agents, service levels, calls waiting, ASA, etc.) provides the intelligence and flexibility required by companies to productively use their resources and effectively service their customers. This capability is vastly superior to simply displaying current operating metrics and hoping a supervisor can decipher what is happening and take the appropriate, correct actions to restore service levels.

While many vendors tout the number of conditions that their routing lexicon provides, what is important is not *how many* conditions they offer, but rather *what conditions* are available to the user. Many conditions serve little purpose in the real world of routing. One example is the use of "available agent" conditions that permit the user to determine if agents are available in some designated group. Keeping in mind that these conditions are used to determine the routing path a transaction will take, why not simply queue the call to the group? If there are available agents the call will be answered. If there are no available agents the call will proceed to the next step in the route. An "available agent" IF statement serves limited purpose and does not generally confer any additional flexibility or control required in today's dynamic contact center environments. It is therefore important for the user to look closely at what is really being offered and what practical applications these conditions will serve to help their business.

A Typical Call Processing Problem

One call processing problem that is fairly typical among contact centers, and highlights the importance of conditional routing, is the situation referred to as "dynamic load balancing between two different applications."

In this example, the contact center receives several different types of calls from their customers. The two primary types of calls are customer service and sales. The goals established are to answer the sales calls with a 90/30 service level (90% of the calls in 30 seconds or less) and to answer customer service calls with a service level goal of 80/30. The agents in these two groups have been cross-trained to handle both types of calls but are much more experienced in handling calls associated with their primary skill. The company wants each group to provide backup for the other but only when it is not at the expense of handling their primary call type. This has created several issues in trying to establish routing that will accomplish that goal. They tried routing to the primary group and then, after 30 seconds of queue, adding the other group. That served little purpose since the company soon realized that given the random nature of incoming calls, a significant number were being handled by agents who did not have that call type as their primary skill. This created longer handling times and, therefore, longer queue times, higher abandoned rates and a degradation of productivity. Worse yet, after a 30-second wait, service level goals were not met when available additional resources could have been brought to bear during that wait.

One Solution

Using the set of conditions in our ideal lexicon, the customer is able to implement a routing scheme that provides the intelligence required to immediately provide backup when service levels are in jeopardy. This is accomplished by examining the current service level of the call type in question and the staffing of the primary agent group to determine if additional resources are needed. Once that determination is made, the routing table checks the service level of the groups brought in to help service the call. If those agents are not achieving the desired service level for their primary call type, they will not be used as a backup. The routing scheme itself provides the balance desired by the customer to ensure that groups not be used as backup at the expense of their primary call types. An example of one way of solving this problem follows:

1. If Sales Service Level < 90%, then go to Step 9
2. Agent Group 1 (Sales)
3. Hold 15 seconds
4. Announcement 1 (First Delay Announcement)
5. Music Source 2
6. Hold 30 seconds
7. Announcement 2 (Second Delay Announcement)
8. Go to Step 6
9. If Sales Agents signed in < 20, then go to Step 11
10. Go to Step 2
11. If Customer Service Service Level < 80%, then go to Step 2
12. Agent Group 1
13. Agent Group 2
14. Go to Step 3

In our example routing table, we can follow the simple, yet powerful, logic applied to processing calls for the sales and customer service agent teams. In step 1, we test for the current service level of the sales application. If the service level is acceptable, control passes to step 2 where we queue for agents in the sales group only. If the service level is not acceptable, control passes to step 9 where a test for the number of agents signed in the sales group takes place. If the number of sales agents is less than 20 we test to determine how well the customer service application is performing prior to potentially offering the sales call to both sales and service groups. If the number of sales agents is greater than 20, queue the sales call only to the sales agent group. In effect, we have created a set of rules that can make automatic adjustments about which agent groups are brought to bear upon sales calls based on the service levels of two applications and the number of signed-on agents in the sales group. Without powerful conditional routing capabilities, a supervisor would have to watch real-time displays and make routing changes based on changing conditions.

This example illustrates the importance of the conditions that can be used in conjunction with the IF statement. The elegant routing solution is possible because conditional routing capabilities can access important metrics like service level and agent group staffing to provide "true dynamic load balancing" between call types and agent groups.

Several factors affect successful implementation and use of conditional routing beyond the ability to be creative and analytical. Users require a clear understanding of the following:
- The segmentation of agents and call types (applications)
- The goals for each department and group
- The conditions available and their implementation
- Examination of information provided by the product to determine the success or failure of the routing solutions being used

While all four are important for success, the last is critical and often overlooked. Many times users will reactively examine the routing only after receiving internal or external complaints. Effective use of conditional routing requires a degree of tuning to achieve optimum performance and needs to be continually examined and modified as business changes and customer patterns affect the contact center.

Skill-Based Routing

Despite the prodigious marketing efforts by many vendors, there are really only two approaches to routing calls to agents. Branding and positioning aside, vendors offer agent skill grouping and/or individual agent skill-based routing. In skill grouping, agents with similar skills are aggregated into a group. In individual agent skill-based routing schemes, each agent has their individual skill profile defined. In skill group routing, when a call arrives to be processed, it is offered to the group or groups best suited to handle the nature of the transaction. In individual agent skill-based routing, when a call arrives, the system creates a virtual group of agents whose profiles make them eligible to handle the nature of the transaction.

Although claims are often made regarding the superiority of one approach over the other, there is practically no empirical data available from actual contact center implementations that support the contention. Most contact center managers tend to believe that individual agent skill-based routing produces superior results. This conclusion is drawn from the supposition that by matching the transaction requirements to the agent's skill, a higher quality, potentially shorter transaction will result.

However, there are some problems associated with this leap of faith.

Agent Population Size Matters

The belief in superior results from individual skill-based routing ignores the impact that agent population size has on the operational results. Mathematical modeling suggests that individual skill-based routing is ineffective when agent populations are relatively small. An accepted contact center fact is that smaller agent groups are inherently inefficient. It is a mistake to take a contact center that has 25 agents and break it into 5 discrete groups of 5 agents each, assuming that forcing more calls into the highly skilled group will improve overall performance.

How Finely Can You Grade Agent Skills, Anyway?

A second serious flaw with individual skill-based routing concerns the actual ability of the contact center management team to measure and define useful and meaningful fine gradations in agent skill along multiple categories. To the extent that the management team cannot produce such fine gradations in skill assessment, individual agent skill-based routing actually becomes an administratively perverse version of skill group routing. I have a really bad feeling that skill profiles are seldom, sometimes never, updated in many contact centers using this technology.

Best Skills Gets Heaviest Workload—Always

Another flaw in individual skill-based routing is the observation that the highest skilled agents will get the heaviest workload. The system can be unrelenting about dealing a call to an agent who just finished one, while another agent sits available doing nothing for minutes on end. But that is one potential outcome of individual agent skill routing. If you are the highest skilled agent in the contact center and many transactions would be best served by you and you alone, rest assured that you will be very busy. Lesser skilled agents will be very much less busy. Left unchecked, individual skill-based routing algorithms can cause burnout among your best agents. For this reason, some vendors have added fairness schemes to the individual skill-based routing algorithms. Ironically, the result is that adding fairness to individual skill-based routing is virtually identical to skill group routing in terms of outcomes.

How Much Can I Really Know About the Transaction?

But the biggest flaw of all has to do with parsing the call, that is, identifying the nature of the transaction. If you can't finely parse the call for transaction nuances, then organizing your agents along a detailed inventory of skill assessments is rather pointless. In contact centers we have precious few tools to help with parsing a call. Dialed Number Identification (DNIS) is one. Automatic Number Identification (ANI) is another. Caller Entered Digits (CED) is yet another tool available. All the tools have inherent or associated problems. Carriers frequently limit the number of DNIS patterns you may define. Dealing with scores, hundreds or thousands of DNIS patterns is a challenging task and tends to complicate contact center reporting. In many cases callers will dial the number they have previously used regardless of the published numbers for different services. This generally creates a need for agents with one skill to screen the call and then transfer it to agents with the skill matching the caller's need. This process increases network time, reduces productivity for the agents, and might be perceived negatively by the caller as they can potentially be queued twice. ANI is useful as far as it goes but the problem is that so many call originate away from home. Thus, the database match ratio for incoming ANI is problematic.

All these shortcomings can be overcome with an elaborate front-end IVR application that presents the caller with menus and submenus. In this fashion, caller's transaction requirements can be finely parsed. The trouble here is that callers are becoming ever more impatient and unhappy with elaborate IVR scripts. The amount of misrouting in elaborate prompting schemes is high and, even more dangerously, subtle enough to go on undetected. There are a surprising number of people in the world who deal with IVR systems by punching out to the first live agent choice presented or intentionally push undefined keys in order to be sent to an attendant.

How Do I Tune the System?

A related problem with individual agent skill routing is more subtle. Suppose you manage to define all your agents' skills along fairly rigorous criteria. You're satisfied that the skill mapping is truly reflective of their abilities. You launch the newly defined routing scheme and, to your horror, several applications show lengthy call queues and high caller abandonments. What do you do? Alter the skill assessments? In what manner? For which agents? If you do that, how will other applications be affected? In my view, creating virtual agent groups on the fly from individually skilled agents invariable means loss of analytical insight by ordinary means. The only solution for this problem is to use a powerful simulation software tool that permits you to model the entire operation. Only by running multiple iterations of calling mix, volume and skill staffing can the contact center manager ever be sure that the right service level outcomes are achieved.

What all this suggests is that while there might be a small advantage for individual skill-based routing schemes in large, complex contact centers, our inability to finely parse the calls and the agent skills squanders that potential. There are virtually no achievable performance differences between skill group and skill-based routing approaches.

Operations Information

It has been suggested that the real value of ACD systems lies not in the call processing, but in the operational data that the machines capture and output. In fact, vendors do tend to directly equate value with the gross number of displays and reports available on their systems. The user is provided a stunning, even overwhelming, array of data as follows:

Trunk Reports
> Calls Offered, Handled & Abandoned
> Average Connect Time
> Trunk Group All Busy Time
> Individual Trunk Statistics
> Out of Service Time

Agent Group Reports
> Average Speed of Answer
> Service Level
> Calls Offered, Handled, Abandoned
> Average Talk Time
> Average After Call Work Time
> Average Number of Staffed Positions
> Average Time to Abandon

Individual Agent Reports
> Sign-On Time
> ACD Calls Handled
> Non-ACD Calls Handled
> Outcalls Placed
> Average Talk Time
> Average After Call Work Time
> Average Idle Time

The user can typically obtain all this kind of data in either real time as it is happening or can ask for printed reports of different historical perspectives. Many systems now support historical records that reach back more than one year.

The irony of all this is that neither the vendors nor the contact center managers are really sure what data should be used in what manner to produce desired results. The philosophy is to provide every kind of report that anyone can imagine to facilitate whatever management practices that might exist. There is much more to say about this subject in the chapters on customer contact metrics and their use. This subject can be temporarily closed by recounting why all this data is necessary.

The Role of Data in Electronic Environments

Imagine that instead of running a contact center, you are managing a grocery store. Apart from all the details connected with putting merchandise on the shelves, there is the management task connected with checking out the customer's cart. You have to worry about lengthy lines, not enough cashiers, no baggers, and a schedule for breaks and lunches. The similarity between the grocery checkout area and a contact center is really close. The cashiers play a role exactly like that of agents while customers wait in line or queues.

There is one huge difference, however, between a checkout manager and a contact center manager. The grocery store is a *physical* store, while the contact center is an *electronic* store. In the physical store, management can use all its senses to dimension conditions, assess alternatives and take corrective actions. In the electronic store management is blind. The contact center represents an invisible world. Management attempts to understand the same kind of dynamics in the contact center as does the checkout manager in a grocery store. However, they use data to furnish their "view."

The trunk reports produced by nearly all systems provide important clues as to whether you have enough trunks, too many trunks and whether they are working properly. Many organizations watch the last trunk in a hunt group closely for the amount of traffic it carries. The logic is that if the last trunk in a hunt group begins to carry increasing amounts of traffic, there is a growing probability that some callers are getting busy signals. Some trunk reports track the amount of time that an entire hunt group is entirely busy. Both numbers can help determine when to add the next trunk. Similarly, many systems have individual trunk reporting. Well-run contact centers look carefully at the average talk time for each trunk in a common group for divergence from average. If a particular trunk is showing a very large difference from average talk time, it can be a signal that callers experience some problem on that trunk that either cuts short or, perversely, lengthens the talk time.

Agent group reports are invaluable. These reports provide data regarding the number of calls offered, handled and abandoned, as well as agent performance statistics such as average talk time, average after call work time, average available time, average idle time and service level or average speed of answer. This data can be used to decide what the demand for access to the contact center is and how well it is being satisfied.

Individual agent reports move one level deeper. Here we see essentially the same kind of data detailed in the group level report for every individual agent in the center. The agents are aggregated by agent group. Armed with this data you can determine a baseline standard for performance by agent group and compare each agent to the group norms. Identification of poorly performing agents is key to the success of any contact center. How to do this and what to do after struggling agents have been identified constitutes a major part of the management process provided in chapter 5.

Historical reports for both trunks, agent groups and individual agents provide guidance in identifying trends and patterns in call demand or any of the other influencing elements that impact service levels. Without this data, a manager can't possibly get in the ballpark, so to speak, regarding staffing levels that relate to service level targets. Ultimately, it doesn't matter how fancy the call processing rules are if there is nobody to talk to the caller.

Once you get into the ballpark by matching call demand with appropriate answer resources, the real-time displays that most systems furnish become useful. Make no mistake about it, if you haven't forecasted call demand and provided for enough staffed positions, the real-time displays will only serve to upset you. Watching a service level disaster unfold in real time on a dispassionate screen is much more painful than going through the disaster blind. If you have forecasted demand and resources you can use the real-time displays to fine-tune your service level. The best forecast can easily diverge from unfolding reality by nearly 10%. We will see how a small perturbation in demand produces huge swings in service level in chapter 5. The real-time displays permit the manager to react to perturbations as they occur instead of letting them ruin the cumulative service level for the day.

Voice Mail

It's nice to keep things simple because there is complexity enough in contact centers. Voice mail is nothing more than a computer system (most likely a PC) running a specialized program. The PC has a digitized human voice encoded on the hard drive. The voice is arranged in segments consisting of whole statements, sentences, phrases and phonemes (literally, word pieces). The specialized software portions the remaining disk into discrete mailboxes; permits mailbox holders to record their voice for greetings; accepts messages from callers; and gives mailbox holders message manipulation capabilities. All the rest consists of details and the devil is in them when you try to select the best system.

It was dismaying to me when voice mail first found its way into the contact center. The entire point of a contact center is to facilitate interactions between the company and its callers. Voice mail has a growing reputation as a barrier to communication rather than an aid. And, there are a few vendors attempting to justify the cost of fancy equipment by advising contact center managers to consciously understaff, relying instead upon voice mail to preserve service levels. In spite of this and some other early misuses, there are excellent applications for voice mail in the contact center.

In general, voice mail can be used to prevent callers from waiting too long. A well-integrated system will let the user treat a collection of voice mail ports as if they were an agent group. The user can include that group of voice mail ports in routing rules so callers have an option after a designated amount of time in queue. The caller may choose whether to remain in queue for a live agent or to leave a voice mail message and receive a callback later. This is an important tool that can help solve *brief* staff-to-call-demand mismatches. Brief is emphasized for reasons detailed shortly.

Using voice mail in a contact center can help build a very positive service image. Callers seem to demand that we accept their call whenever it suits them. Even if a contact center is unable to provide human answer resources, many callers expect this kind of automation to make it simple and convenient for them. Voice mail has never been more affordable and if your contact center has some number of internal employees calling as part of the call demand, there are few better tools available. Internal employees can be trained to use voice mail effectively and, with repeated use, will come to trust time-delayed voice exchanges whereas many casual callers will not.

There can also be applications for individual agent voice mailboxes, particularly in claims processing. Often, any appropriately skilled agent can handle an initial claims call. But if the transaction requires subsequent calls and interactions, it might be more efficient for the caller to speak with the same agent. Return calls to a particular agent will frequently find that agent already engaged. Therefore, individual agent mailboxes can be valuable. One requirement for stand-alone ACD systems is that they should interface with the associated PBX's voice mail system so call center agents don't have one voice mail system while the rest of the enterprise uses another.

There are just a few potential problems associated with voice mail in the contact center. One is referred to as "the contact center death spiral," the other involves the speed of the callback. Whenever you invite a caller to leave a message in a contact center environment, you must make the callback within a reasonable time. The trouble is: What's reasonable? Well, it depends. Are you the only game in town? How much does the company really care? What do your competitors do? But in any case, a good rule of thumb is that a callback should be made within an hour. Although, sooner would be better. The risk you run after taking the message is that the caller will get antsy and place *another* call. There is a chance that the second call attempt will end up in voice mail as well! Now you have an upset caller and two separate messages. Your agent force will callback twice, further upsetting the caller. None of this is particularly cost-effective.

The "contact center death spiral" is the effect of voice mail on contact center reporting. Suppose that I am responsible for forecasting call demand and arranging appropriate staffing levels. I work exclusively with calls offered, handled, abandoned, average talk time and average after call work time. I don't have visibility into how well voice mail message retrieval and callbacks are being managed. Furthermore, suppose that one day an unexpected increase in call demand causes more callers to go to voice mail than previously. Because it takes far less time for a caller to leave a message than to actually complete the transaction, at the end of the day I notice that the average talk time is lower than usual, the call load is higher and the service level is still good. I would naturally predict that the call load will return to more normal proportions but might assume that the reduction in talk time would persist. The motivation sessions must be working, I rationalize. So, consulting my Erlang tables I would find that the reduction in talk time permits a decrease in staffing by a few agents. The next day with lower staffing, more callers go to voice mail. The average talk time drops more. This leads to reduced staffing which leads to more voice messages. If driven to ridiculous proportions, we would see this contact center staffed with no agents, all callers going to voice mail, the average talk time equal to the average message length and a service level that looked great. This probably can't happen in reality. A useful lesson is to be relentless about anything that could potentially warp management data—there are dangerous consequences.

Interactive Voice Response

IVR is always a plus in the contact center. Again, the basic technology is fairly simple. A PC runs an application similar to voice mail in that part of the hard drive that has digitized human voice on it. The difference is that the application has access to either its own database or to another computer system database. The IVR system uses speech to guide callers through the application. The caller uses the system by pressing the buttons on their touch-tone telephone. The IVR system can retrieve certain kinds of information from a database and speak the data to the caller.

In contact centers, IVR systems are used to prompt callers for more information that can refine the call processing rules for that call. IVR can help route callers to the proper agent. And, IVR can complete callers' transaction requests for information. This frees human agents to handle more complex transactions. The justification for IVR lies in its ability to handle some transactions more economically than human agents. Even if your company can't afford 24-hour customer service, an IVR system can provide certain valuable customer service functions all the time. They are tireless, affordable and there is growing caller acceptance.

The shift in caller attitude toward IVR has been astounding. In general, IVR acceptance is related to caller demographics. The older the caller, the less likely they will be to judge IVR routines as pleasing and satisfactory. One of the cardinal rules in IVR scripting is to always permit callers to escape to a human agent. One of the early users of IVR frequently witnessed agents being connected to callers bellowing about the indignity of being forced to talk to a machine. But recently, while monitoring calls coming into a financial institution, one caller complained to an agent that he wanted to be handled by a machine. This seems to be the case particularly in the financial industry. For example, some customers have trouble keeping the balance straight on their accounts. If they call and talk to a human agent, over time they will be identified by the agents as a frequent caller. Talking with a machine confers a sense of privacy upon the transaction that more and more people value.

The only potential problem associated with IVR has to do with the menu process. Speech is relatively slow and serial. IVR vendors caution users to limit the digit reply choices to between 3 and 5 items in any menu level. As users dream up new applications, sometimes the menu process becomes too much of a burden. One of the worst examples ever encountered was in a governmental agency. The menu process was timed from start to completion. Listening to menu choices and pressing buttons took nearly two and a half minutes!

Happily, technology is now available that promises to reinvent IVR applications and transform them into more pleasing interactions. The newest wrinkle in IVR technology is natural language, speaker independent, voice recognition. Computer processors have become fast enough and software algorithms have become smart enough for computers to listen to human voice and figure out what the caller is saying. "Voice reco," as it is sometimes referred to, is amazing technology. Vendors create libraries of phonemes, words and phrases of particular interest in an application. Hundreds of people are recruited to say the phonemes, words and phrases so that a digitized template can be created for each element. Using a large population of speakers helps ensure that the digitized template will properly decode spoken words and phrases regardless of accent, pronunciation or tone.

An IVR application that is augmented by natural language, speaker independent, voice recognition is fundamentally different from a traditional IVR application. In traditional IVR routines, the system rattles out an initial menu of choices and asks the caller to depress a digit on the telephone keypad. There are often multiple layers of menus and it is easy to get confused or forget choice options. With voice recognition, IVR routines are more like ordinary conversation. The IVR asks questions instead of presenting menus. The caller speaks their responses instead of pressing keys. The IVR routine will periodically restate what it understands to that point and ask the caller if the accumulated information is correct.

Some of the better voice recognition IVR routines I have encountered are almost eerie. It is as if I am speaking with a person. Not only is this efficient, it is very pleasing. My hands are free since I don't have to press keys on the phone. Since my interaction is entirely verbal, I can keep my eyes on the tasks that require them, like driving down the expressway. Speaker-independent voice recognition is the best thing to happen to IVR systems since touch-tone signaling. I believe that this technology will reinvigorate IVR application thinking and further expand acceptance.

Workforce Management Software Systems

Workforce management systems (WFM) are available in a broad range of capabilities and sophistication. These software packages are concerned with forecasting call volumes based on historical data; calculating required staff given a desired service level goal, taking into account individual agent's preferences for work patterns and days off; and creating a set of individual schedules. This software attempts to minimize the labor involved in providing a desired service level while maximizing agent shift preferences.

The problems associated with staffing and scheduling are better described as horrors. A contact center manager is caught between two demanding factions: callers and agents. The callers demand good service. Moreover, they expect good service whenever it is convenient for them to place the call, to have their calls answered quickly and to obtain factual, crisp information. Agents demand a reasonable working environment, recognition as individuals and some degree of latitude with respect to work hours. As agents gain employment seniority and increase their job knowledge, they tend to expect more flexibility from their employers.

As a contact center manager, you try to balance these two factions every half-hour of every day. You can attempt to maximize your service level and minimize your labor expense if you can manage to keep agents on the phone from the moment they sign-in until the end of their shifts. No breaks. No lunches. No lives. On the other hand, you can maximize the good will of your staff by permitting them to work schedules that are totally convenient for them without regard for the call demand. Somewhere between those poles lies the best solution.

Workforce management software packages tend to be organized along similar lines. The system may collect data from an ACD system by interfacing to a printer or supervisor port. More recently, WFM systems are capable of fetching necessary data directly from the operations database maintained by the ACD system. Operational data can be organized along 15-, 30- or 60-minute intervals. The shorter the data window, the more precise the forecasts will be. As the software package collects data, it builds a model of that contact center's operating environment. The software database captures all the myriad patterns that all contact centers experience. Call arrival patterns exist based on time of day, day of week, day of month and month of year. Armed with this historical data and cognizant of all the patterns, workforce management software is capable of producing call volume forecasts with amazing precision.

WFM systems use different techniques to predict future call volume. Some reduce call volume history to a so-called "model." The model approach to forecasting seems to be less precise than others because changes in call volume or arrival patterns have to persist over many days before the model fully takes account of the changes. Many systems use recent history to predict call volumes. This is a better approach to forecasting than offered by the model approach. A flaw in some systems is that they don't differentiate between days of the week and days of the month. That is, the best forecast for the third Monday of next month will tend to weigh the last several third Mondays of the previous months, rather than simply the last several Mondays. The day of the week and the position of the day in the month and year are very important in achieving high-precision forecasts.

Once a call-volume forecast has been created, the next step is to calculate the number of staffed positions that will be required to meet the service level target. Nearly all systems use some variation of the Erlang C statistical formula to accomplish the calculation. While other statistical approaches exist, Erlang C has survived the test of time. It is a well-behaved algorithm with a slight tendency to overstaff. This tendency is well understood and turns out to be very valuable, since agents seldom achieve perfect schedule adherence. Alternatively, where skill routing has been implemented and skill scheduling is necessary, Erlang C has proved to be less desirable and less accurate than simulation. Where complex skill environments exist, simulation routines are used to mimic the mix of call types and each type's arrival patterns so that the correct number of agents with the appropriate skill sets are on hand. Because there will be tardiness and absences, most contact centers rely on the very slight overstaffing tendency to provide a cushion to help ensure high service levels.

Once the forecast and required staff is calculated, most WFM systems figuratively turn their attention to the agents. A major part of the complexity of these software systems has to do with work rules and agent preferences. The user defines what kind of work patterns are acceptable. There are many permutations and combinations of total shift length, number of breaks, length of breaks, meal breaks, and so on. Defining work patterns involves deciding when permissible start times shall occur, how long after the start time the first break should be scheduled, how long the agent should work after the last break before ending the shift, and so on.

Before the system can start assigning agents into the call-demand matrix, better systems permit supervisors to enter schedule exceptions. Life would be much simpler if agents just answered calls and did nothing else. But that's almost never the case, particularly in blended, multimedia contact centers. Besides very different types of transactions, lunches and breaks, agents require recurring training. They also have doctor appointments, off-phone activities, vacations and a number of other schedulable activities. Better WFM systems permit supervisors to plan ahead for these activities so ensuing schedules will more accurately reflect true agent availability.

After scheduled exceptions are entered, the WFM system is fully prepared to match caller demand with agent availability. Using near-magical software routines, the system begins to place agent work patterns into the required staff matrix. This is a highly reiterative process. The software is attempting to place agents into the demand matrix to achieve the best coverage for the call load while granting senior agents their work preferences. Usually the most senior agents are scheduled first. After all the full-time agents have been scheduled, part-time agents can be scheduled to fill gaps, plug holes and provide coverage during breaks and lunches.

In a perfect world, WFM systems could stop there. Agents would always follow their individual schedules without fail and the actual call demand would be identical to the forecasted call volume. Alas, that is never the case. After agents schedules have been generated, it is frequently the case that some agents will want to swap schedules or slightly alter their own schedules to meet obligations that could not have been predicted and planned for. As a result, most WFM systems have a number of schedule-management routines.

Not only is it rare for agents to achieve perfect schedule adherence, but the call demand almost always refuses to precisely match the forecast. These two dynamics yield to a process called automatic intraday refore-casting. The idea behind this process is that no matter how good a forecaster I am, it is easier to predict today's high temperature after observing the temperature climb through the morning hours than it would be to predict today's high temperature sometime last week. So, some WFM systems accept data from the ACD system as each half-hour period ends regarding call volume and transaction time to produce refined and much more accurate call volume and transaction time forecasts for the balance of the day. And because the WFM system knows exactly how many agents are present, precise service level projections can be calculated. This permits managers and supervisors to make informed judgments about short-term changes in center staffing.

Finally, WFM systems produce reports that provide feedback to the forecaster, supervisors and agents. For the forecaster, the system provides insight into whether the machine or the human forecaster produced the more accurate forecast. Feedback sharpens the forecaster's skills. It is important to recognize that forecasting call volume is part science and part art. The artful side of forecasting requires information feedback to improve the process. For supervisors, the system provides a kind of scorecard that identifies how well that supervisor's agents are adhering to their schedules. For the agent, the system provides feedback about how well they are following the schedules that have been created for them. In most contact centers, the difference between world-class service and poor service is frequently a matter of a few incremental staffed positions at the right time. Schedule adherence is frequently the difference between success and failure in the contact center.

Who needs workforce management? Nearly any center with more than 50 agents or any size center with extended hours.

Quality Monitoring Systems

Later in this book we have a lot to say about measuring quality. In my view, measuring and managing quality represents one of the more important tasks that a contact center management team can undertake because the payback is so potentially large. The manual process described later really works. Many contact centers use such a process or a variation thereof. The biggest single problem associated with quality measurement is the time commitment required by the quality monitors or supervisors. Measuring quality involves listening to calls. Invariably, in order to obtain one good scoreable call, the quality control supervisor will have to listen to multiple calls. This inflates the time required to accomplish the task.

Responding to this need, several vendors have specialized in creating systems that help reduce the time requirement and improve the scoring process. This is done by using some voice mail technology together with sophisticated application software. In effect, their system interfaces into ACD systems as if it was a supervisor invoking the ubiquitous "silent monitoring" supervisor feature. The quality monitoring software system is given a schedule of agent shifts and a guideline as to how many quality samples per agent are desired. The system automatically and randomly records conversations by agent. At a later time, the quality monitor or supervisor can access the stored conversations. The supervisor has complete control over the replay and is usually provided a screen that guides the quality scoring process.

The goal of the quality monitoring software is to produce a set of quality scores by agent to augment the many productivity metrics that contact center technology routinely provides. Quality scores, combined with productivity scores, help enlightened contact center management teams perform critical coaching tasks more effectively. These software systems also typically provide some analysis of the quality monitors or supervisors themselves to help ensure that scores among various monitors are correlated and that no biases are creeping into the judgmental scoring.

More recently, quality-monitoring software has broadened in scope to include real-time views of the agent's screen as it responds to keyboard manipulations. The systems are interfaced into the local area network. In this way, when a supervisor replays the agent's conversation, they also see a replay of the agent's screen. Thus, the quality monitor obtains a 360-degree view of the agent performing a transaction. Not only is the conversation captured, but the keystrokes and screens accessed by the agent during the conversation are revealed. This is very helpful in the coaching process because an agent's productivity is often impaired by computer navigation issues rather than call control skills.

The justification for quality monitoring software is rather straightforward: It saves monitor's time. As contact centers get bigger, the time requirements associated with manual quality monitoring become a problem. In fact, the time commitment is the single biggest reason why quality scoring is either entirely lacking or is calculated on such a small per-agent sample that the scores become suspect.

Computer Telephony Integration

Even though some industry analysts have pronounced CTI dead, I still find it to be the most interesting part of contact center technology today. It was inevitable that as contact center technologies became more computer-like, someone would discover advantageous applications involving information exchange between the devices. As computers became more powerful and multiprocessor technology emerged, it became practical for the switch to process calls, collect data, report the data *and* carry on data exchanges with another computer systems.

Before CTI links, the only connecting point between the switching system and the computer system driving the agent terminals was the agent. The agent reacted to data supplied by the ACD system and used the data processing system to handle the transaction request. For example, the ACD system can inform the agent, via their agent instrument display, the DNIS number dialed by that caller. Still, the agent must work the computer keyboard to bring up the appropriate transaction screen and that takes time.

With a CTI link installed and appropriate software running on the IT side, the ACD system can pass the DNIS digits and the agent position number of the agent to the local area network. The LAN system software can use those pieces of information to automatically display the correct transaction type screen upon the correct agent display. This saves precious seconds for each transaction. As we shall see in the section about contact center dynamics, seconds saved in a transaction have dramatic operational results.

Beyond DNIS lies the almost magical applications involving the combination of ANI and CTI links. In this application, the ACD receives the calling party's telephone number. The system sends this data together with the agent's position identifier. The computer system can use the originating telephone number as an access key into the customer database. If there is a match, the computer can paint customer data on the screen in front of the agent as the caller's voice enters the agent's ear. Knowing who is calling before you answer facilitates big time savings. You can avoid smarmy nonspecific greetings, the questions and replies required to identify the calling party and the keyboard time and the computer response time associated with the identification process.

There are two distinct types of CTI enablement: first-party and third-party. I think that more people are familiar with third-party CTI. Third-party CTI always involves a CTI server that, in turn, has access to enterprise databases as required. In third-party CTI, information about the number dialed, what number is calling or who actually is calling is passed from the ACD to the CTI server. The CTI server uses this data to retrieve information about the caller and to launch the correct transaction processing routine automatically on behalf of the agent.

In first-party CTI there is no server involved. As a result, these applications cost far less and can be implemented in a relatively short time. Most first-party routines require a soft phone to be provisioned on the agent's desktop. The manner in which this works is straightforward, yet elegant. DNIS or ANI information is presented on the display of the agent's soft phone. A desktop software process cuts this data from the softphone display and pastes it into the appropriate place in the transaction processing routine as if the agent had keyed the data in as normal. The result is that the application fetches the appropriate information and presents it to the agent by the time the agent's standard greeting is finished. As in third-party CTI processes, time is saved by not having to ask questions and enter replies to access the caller's data.

Some analysts have stated that the CTI industry is dead because CTI is an enabling technology rather than an end in itself. Beyond this, CTI projects have often failed to deliver their original promise or have ended up costing far more dollars and taking much more time than planned. These very real problems have less to do with the technology than with human dynamics. Even now, the IT department and the contact center have little understanding of each other's complexities, issues and problems. The biggest problems facing CTI projects are a lack of clear understanding of what is to be accomplished and what the current operating environment actually is. Moreover, while there is a measurable benefit associated with "screen pops," more contact center managers understand that what is really needed is to re-engineer the way work is performed.

So many contact center software applications used by agents are actually older pieces of software developed in mainframe computer days. They have been updated slightly by being ported into Microsoft Windows environments but no rework of the screen layouts or screen flows is undertaken. As contact center applications proliferate and expand, agents are eventually confronted with a myriad of screens drawing data from a variety of sources. This situation demands extra agent training and ultimately causes the performance of the center to hit a wall beyond which the team cannot get. This is discussed further in the section on Desktop Re-Engineering.

In the final analysis, CTI is not dead at all. If it were not for CTI, there would be no Customer Relationship Management (CRM) industry to fill up industry trade press publications with adverts and vendor-written calls for action. There is more to say about CRM in a later section.

Here is one final thought about CTI projects and CRM in general. The advice given to Benjamin in the film *The Graduate* was simply "plastics." The advice to contact center managers is simply "database." CTI projects will fail and Customer Relationship Management cannot be practiced until and unless the organization has a very good, thorough database of information about their customers. These databases must, by necessity, be rich in detail. Today, you need at least three phone numbers in every customer profile: home, work and mobile telephone numbers. You need several e-mail address data fields since many people have a business account and a personal, private Internet account. Beyond basics like these, a business needs to understand how their customers segment themselves. Who are the best customers? Who are the worst customers? Are you sure you even know how to answer that question?

A screen-pop is a useful technique to help contact centers gain efficiency. However, to secure much larger benefits from CTI technologies a firm has to invest in segmentation, process integration and stringent database practices.

Virtual Contact Centers

There are several ways a firm can find itself confronting the special problems associated with running multiple contact centers. Acquisitions and mergers frequently lead to multiple contact centers, usually of different manufacture. Even without merger and acquisition activity, many firms find that business growth demands significant expansion of contact center technology. From a practical sense, organizations consider a range of call handling options along an axis that could be depicted as in figure 4-5.

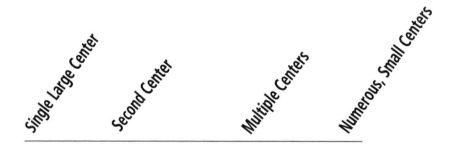

Figure 4-5. Range of Call Handling Options

The overwhelming factor in moving from left to right on the size axis is economic. There are other issues involved, such as disaster recovery and time zone coverage. However, among the several economic considerations the most significant is agent labor costs. A demonstration case was created to illustrate the source and magnitude of potential agent labor savings.

The case assumes an average talk time of 240 seconds (4 minutes). We also assume an average after call work time of 20 seconds. Thus, the aggregate transaction time is 260 seconds. In our case, we assume that the enterprise expects to receive 4,500 calls in a particular 30-minute period of the day. The goal of the enterprise is to attempt to answer 80% of these calls within 20 seconds of arrival. Erlang C statistical tables were used to derive staffing requirements and predict certain call center performance metrics. The call volume of 4,500 calls was simulated in software against the following configurations:
1. A single large call center
2. Three (3) call centers
3. Twenty (20) call centers
4. Four hundred (400) call centers

The results of the calculations are provided in the following table:

Number of Centers	Required Agents	Reduction in Agents	ASA	Service Level	Occ.	Prob. Delay	Delay Delayed
400	1,600		15.9 sec	88.3%	43.3%	13.9%	114.7 sec
20	760	840	12.3 sec	82.8%	85.5%	26.1%	47.2 sec
3	681	919	9.5 sec	82.9%	95.4%	37.8%	25.1 sec
1	663	937	10 sec	81.5%	98.0%	50.1%	20.0 sec

The phenomenon associated with the pooling of labor in call centers is well understood. In the above chart, each call center operates independently and handles its portion of the total call load of 4,500. That is: Each of the three call centers handles 1,500 calls; each of the 20 call centers handles 225 calls; and each of the 400 call centers handles 12 calls each in a 30-minute period. Then, the individual site figures are reaggregated for the enterprise.

We clearly see that required agent labor declines sharply from 400 centers of 4 agents per center to 20 centers of 38 agents per center to 3 centers of 227 agents per center and, finally, a single center with 663 agents. Notice that the rate of labor savings decreases as the sites consolidate. Notice that the occupancy of the agents increases as the centers become larger. Notice that the probability that a random caller will experience a delay increases as the centers become larger, but that the delay these callers will likely experience shortens as the centers grow larger.

As the required agent labor is reduced through consolidation, so too are ancillary labor requirements. Agents have to have supervisors. More centers require more agents who need more supervisors. To a lesser degree, as we progress in consolidation we also require less management and technical support overhead.

In short, economics drive call center consolidation. But, there is a counterargument to consolidation. As a contact center becomes larger, it becomes harder to run. As the size of the center increases, a disabling anonymity among the work force takes hold. Factions emerge. Personal human dynamics begin to work against the benefits of resource pooling. The physical plant becomes an issue. Parking spaces for so many agents across multiple shifts requires significant acreage. Contact centers have a high people/area ratio. Access becomes an issue. Security becomes an issue. When centers become massive, it is no longer possible to use commercial eating facilities located around the center. Internal cafeteria services have to be provided. Even daycare becomes an issue.

Having said all that, the largest problem confronting single large contact centers is labor availability. Contact centers have been created in unprecedented numbers. Coupled with a robust economy, many areas of the world are faced with a shortage of available contact center agents. The result is a fierce competition among contact center users for trained, productive agents. This creates wage inflation and drives up training costs as the center operator is faced with unrelenting new-hire training requirements.

So, some dynamics favor consolidation into a single center and some favor multiple, somewhat smaller centers. Since the pooling principle is well understood, even when firms choose to deploy multiple centers, they configure them so that some sharing of call volume can be accomplished. Consequently, the next area of discussion is about how multiple contact centers can operate.

Virtual Centers—Count the Ways

Organizations that deploy multiple contact centers can configure them in a variety of ways. And, because this is a large, lucrative and growing market, there is an interesting competition developing among two camps; the intelligent network camp and the intelligent customer premise equipment camp. For more than 20 years, customer premises equipment (CPE) has held sway in the marketplace. Those vendors have added sophisticated features and provided administrative and management tools at an unprecedented rate. As a result, CPE vendors have realized significant revenues and market share. Intelligent network vendors naturally take notice of significant markets. For the past 10 years, they have been working to deliver more and more features, functions and benefits that directly compete with CPE features, functions and benefits. So the ensuing discussion has to be taken in two parallel paths. First, we will examine how intelligent network features can be used to create virtual call centers. Then we'll look at how CPE vendors have responded.

In a general sense, multisite call centers become more and more virtual (by that I mean that multiple sites act more and more like a single site). We can categorize this progression along the following axis:

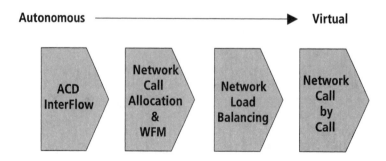

Figure 4-6. Progressively More Virtual Operations

An enterprise can choose to operate multiple centers autonomously or can link them to share the workload to a greater and greater degree. This part of the discussion will focus on solutions involving the intelligent public-switched voice network. It is difficult to frame this discussion without briefly reviewing how the public-switched network works with respect to connecting 800 calls.

The Intelligent Network

For quite some time all the major interexchange carriers such as AT&T, Worldcom and Sprint have operated two networks: the voice network we all know and a data network called Signaling System 7. We can depict the modern telephone network with respect to 800 calling as follows:

Figure 4-7. 800 Network Operation

When a caller, represented in the drawing as the handset near Florida, calls our 800 number in a multisite environment, the call moves to the nearest Class IV Point of Presence (POP) for the interexchange carrier controlling that 800 number. The voice portion of that call gets parked at the POP while a data message is sent to the interexchange carrier's Service Control Point (SCP). The SCP is a complex database that uses the number that was dialed and the number placing the call to determine what real telephone number the call attempt should be routed to. Some people are surprised to discover that 800 numbers are fictitious and exist mainly as billing mechanisms.

Once the SCP has determined what real telephone number to route the call to, a return data message is sent to the Class IV POP. Now the Class IV switch "knows" where to send the call. In a multisite environment, part of the SCP database for our enterprise will consist of a list of origination area codes that point to a particular call center location. This is called area code allocation. In our example above, we have three call centers. One is located in the Northeast, one in the South, and one in the West. In our diagram, we can imagine that the Florida caller might be allocated to the call center in the Northeast. In similar fashion, the second caller in the diagram (located in the Southwest) could dial the exact same 800 number but would always be routed to the call center in the West.

All the leading interexchange carriers provide varying levels of tools to their users to control how the SCP routes 800 call attempts. In addition to simple area code allocation, users can identify time of day routing changes. At different times of day or day of week, the area code allocation rules are altered. This permits users to route all calls to the East Coast center in the morning when the agents are there, and route all calls to the West Coast center in the evening when its agents are there. In this way, firms avoid shift premiums for nontraditional hours. Similarly, enterprises can shut down multiple sites during off-peak night hours and send all call attempts to a single site operated around the clock.

In addition to area code allocation, the carriers provide different levels of control over the allocation rules in the SCP. At the lowest level, users can telephone a contact to request changes in the routing rules. Generally, these telephone requests take effect within 30 minutes. Obviously, this time lag can create operational problems in highly dynamic environments. For these customers, the carriers have provided for direct online access to the routing rules engine in the SCP. With online access, users can alter the rules in near real time so as to react to changing call patterns and staffing levels in their call centers.

It is fair to say that the intelligent network, in regard to 800 calling, is becoming very much like an ACD in the sky. A user can have some call processing performed before the call ever connects to an answer point. In the past few years, the interexchange carriers have added IVR (interactive voice response) to their network services. With this capability, callers dialing an 800 number can be routed to a carrier IVR system and queried for additional information about their transaction requirements. The responses keyed or spoken by the caller are referred to as "Caller Entered Digits." This information permits the user and the carrier to refine the allocation of the caller to a particular site or to conduct a simple IVR query process in the same way as if done at a customer premise.

All the services provided by interexchange carriers tend to be priced on a "per-transaction" basis. That is: Each change to the area code allocation tables has a price; each call handled by a network IVR has a price. Pricing is all over the scale. Although tariffs are in place, the interexchange carriers have created a "Let's Make a Deal" environment. As a result, it can be difficult to plan in the abstract without engaging in some dialog with the carrier of your choice.

How Virtual Do You Want to Be?

After this very brief overview of how the intelligent network operates, we need to return to the range of interconnection options available to a multisite call center user.
- Totally Autonomous
- ACD Interflow
- Network Call Allocation & Workforce Management Integration
- Network Load Balancing
- Network Call by Call Routing

Totally Autonomous

There are enterprises that operate multiple centers in a totally autonomous fashion. Each center operates independent from the others. This makes sense only when the applications within the call center are wholly contained within a single center. This frequently comes about when the call demand associated with an application is not large and can be handled by the agents in a single center. Another way this comes about is when the data for an application resides in only one location or when external issues, such as regulations or licensing, limit agents in other locations from becoming involved in the application. It is fair to say that the number of firms that operate multiple sites in an autonomous fashion is relatively small.

ACD Interflow

The first level of center interconnection involves ACD interflow. If you only have two sites, this might be as much interconnection as you will ever need. Recall from the discussion on intelligent networks that many firms use area code allocation to portion the total call demand among their sites. Since calls are placed in a random fashion, it can happen that a single center begins to experience an increased rate of call arrivals. Left to its own, that center will experience lengthened call queues and increasing call abandon rates. Rather than change the area code allocation rules (because of cost issues or time delays), ACD systems have developed interflow software. This feature set has been developed by ACD vendors because interexchange carriers charge their customers for the tools and access that permits them to alter area code allocation rules. More importantly, many users have developed a very good understanding of their unique call demand patterns and see no point in changing the routing rules for what they consider short-term perturbations in call demand at one particular site.

Interflow schemes involve using telephone circuits to link the sites in a limited fashion. Coupled with the physical links is relatively sophisticated software routines that, in effect, query the other sites to determine whether they are in a position to accept a call from the overburdened site. We can depict an interflow scheme as follows:

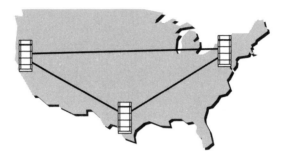

Figure 4-8. Contact Center Interflow Scheme

In our three-site configuration we see that each site is linked with circuits to each other site. Typically, T-1 or ISDN spans are used. These circuits are separate and distinct from the circuits that bring the callers into the sites.

Suppose that, for some reason, the site in the Northeast begins to experience a much higher call arrival rate than is normally the case. The routing rules for that site will have been set up so that when the queue time begins to exceed predefined limits, the ACD seizes one of the inter-flow circuits connected to the other two sites. The other two sites have routing rules established within them that notice the interflow request. They look at the state of their own queues and the agents groups within themselves to determine whether they are in a position to accept an over-flow call. This is important because it makes no sense to move a caller from the Northeast site to some other site unless we reasonably expect that the caller will be serviced sooner at the other site. After all, it will cost us some incremental money to move that call.

These interflow routing schemes need to be intelligent because users want to guard against the possibility that all the sites are experiencing unexpectedly heavy traffic and all begin to ship callers to other sites. Were that to happen, the user would be incurring incremental transmission costs for no gain.

Interflow schemes are widely used by many enterprises that operate multiple call centers. Often, T-1 or ISDN spans already exist between the sites as part of the data communications infrastructure. Since these facilities provide multiple paths, it is likely that the data communications requirements will not completely fill the span, which leaves some number of paths available for voice call interflow. Essentially, the voice interflows are free.

There are issues connected with interflow. Consideration must be given to how often interflow will likely occur and how many simultaneous interflow calls are likely to be moved. There are few things more frustrating than when a single site is grossly overloaded with queued calls, the other sites are lightly loaded but there are not enough paths to move the aging calls to where they can be answered. Another issue is how the systems report on interflow calls. Often, interflow schemes encounter situations where all the sites are busy and there are no available agents anywhere. In this case the interflow requests are held at each site. The caller is still queued physically at the original site while call interflow requests are pending at the other sites. The caller is now queued for the next available agent across all three locations. Eventually, an agent becomes available at some site and the caller is connected. The issue of interest is how the other systems treat the withdrawn interflow request. Some systems cannot tell the difference between a withdrawn interflow request and an abandoned call, others can. When ACD systems cannot differentiate between the two cases, management information becomes corrupted and abandoned call reporting becomes unreliable. More important, some systems inflate call attempt counts, which makes call forecasting much more difficult and increases the probability for error.

Network Call Allocation and Workforce Management Integration

The next level of site interconnection involves the marriage of two contact center technologies. Recall that the SCP can be programmed to change the area code allocations among the multiple sites. It can also be programmed to simply portion calls among the sites. This is called percent allocation. Thus, we can have the SCP programmed to deliver 100% of all the calls in the nation to the East Coast center in the early morning when the agents are arriving at work there. Then, when agents begin arriving at the Southern center, we can have the SCP split the call load between the two staffed sites. Later, when agents begin to arrive at work at the West Coast center we can have the SCP split the call load between all three sites. During the late afternoon a reverse procedure takes place. That is the science of percent allocation. The art of percent allocation lies in figuring out what percentages to use for the sites. Many firms have dedicated staff to watch how the sites are performing and make minor adjustments to the percent allocations during the day. The problem with all this is that changes in the percent allocations do not take effect instantly. So managing traffic among multiple sites becomes very much like piloting a huge supertanker. Changes made at the helm take some time to have effect and it becomes increasingly likely that the enterprise ends up on the rocks, from a service level standpoint.

What the traffic controllers are reacting to, of course, is the agent staffing and performance at the multiple sites. Happily, there are software packages in use at many call centers that focus on staffing and performance: Workforce Management software packages.

These software packages, available from several vendors, use ACD call load history to predict the call load for a future week. The package permits the users to establish performance goals, usually expressed in terms of service level. Agent preferences are established in the database. Most firms permit tenured agents to identify which work patterns they prefer. Usually, an agent is provided the opportunity to identify several work patterns in a rank ordering. The magic of workforce management is that the software produces a forecast of the expected call volume for each 30-minute period of the day and produces a set of agent schedules that match up to that call volume. The agent schedules specify start times, break times, lunch times, even training and meeting times. The software's ability to produce close matches between agents staffing and call volume is closely linked with the number of full- and part-time agents employed by the enterprise. Typically, the full-time staff is layered in first and the part-time agents are used to meet peak traffic times during the day. You can clearly see that multiple call sites help this process since breaks and lunches across time zones provides the scheduling software greater flexibility.

One final element of workforce management software: Even if we are lucky enough to produce a perfect fit of schedules to call demand, it is unlikely that agent schedules will be adhered to perfectly. People get sick, have accidents on the way to work, their alarm clocks fail to go off and so on. Therefore, most workforce management packages have a feature called schedule exceptions and intraday reforecasting. When an agent calls in sick or with a delay, that information can be entered into the software. Likewise, as the day begins to progress and the call demand becomes evident, the software might discover that there is going to be a significant difference between the forecasted and actual call volumes for that day. Schedule exceptions and intraday reforecasts will tell management if they need to call more agents in to work or whether they can send some agents home or handle more nonvoice transactions. Among multiple sites, the software can also determine how the call load should be portioned among the sites.

We can depict this configuration below:

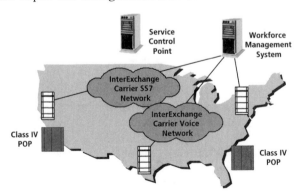

Figure 4-9. WFM-Driven Virtual System

In this configuration, the workforce management system is connected to each site. Typically, supervisors have access to some of the modules so that they can enter schedule exceptions as they occur. At some central location, the WFM planners run intraday reforecasts that consider schedule exceptions, as well as refine the forecasted call volume for that day. The outcome is a set of accurate percent allocations that can be used in the SCP to portion the calls among the various sites. Many enterprises have achieved excellent operational results with this combination of techniques. When coupled with ACD interflow, this configuration becomes nearly as efficient as a single, huge call center without suffering the negative consequences associated with a single, large center.

Network Load Balancing and Network Call-by-Call Routing

For the purposes of this discussion, we will combine these two techniques since they use the same processes and differ only in degree. Recall that intelligent network routing of 800 calls comes about through the programming of the SCP. We have discussed techniques to alter the rules in the SCP thus far. In the last few years, with the advent of 800 number portability among interexchange carriers, the SCP has been "opened up." That is: End users can create and operate their own SCP. Instead of the interexchange carrier's SCP making the routing decisions, users can deploy hardware and software that interacts and talks with the carrier's SCP. In effect, the interexchange carrier's SCP hands off the routing decision to the user's SCP. This can be illustrated as follows:

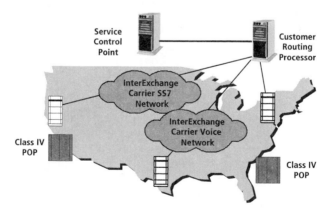

Figure 4-10. 800 Call Routing via Customer Routing Processor

In a load-balancing implementation, simple percent allocation is programmed at the interexchange carrier's SCP. The user's SCP is properly called a "Customer Routing Processor" or CRP. The SCP literally counts calls and a small portion of the calls are referred to the CRP for destination routing. Keep in mind that these are data messages we are talking about and not actual calls. The caller is physically held at the POP nearest that caller and all this is taking place in less than a second.

Note that the CRP has high-speed data links to each call center. In this way, the CRP has a constant picture of the state of each site. In typical deployment models, the SCP is directing 80 to 90% of the calls based on percent allocations. The CRP is directing the remaining 10% or 20% of the calls. Since the CRP "sees" what is actually going on in real time, it can detect a hot spot developing at one site and direct its portion of the calls to the site or sites with spare capacity. Since the CRP is doing this in real time, the effect is a kind of self-correcting, automatic interflow performed at the network level.

The reason that typical deployments don't have the CRP handling larger portions of the total call load is that interexchange carriers typically charge the user a per-call fee when they want to use their own CRP. These fees are highly negotiable depending upon a user's total amount of 800 traffic and their willingness to dedicate that traffic to a single interexchange carrier over long contract periods. Nevertheless, the per-call fee structure acts as an economic disincentive to route all the 800 traffic through your own CRP.

A few enterprises have implemented full call-by-call routing performed in their own CRP. In this case, the interexchange carrier's SCP makes no routing decisions at all. All call destination decisions are referred to the user's CRP. While this might seem expensive, it is a highly useful solution for enterprises that have fully embraced skill-based routing. Since the CRP "sees" exactly what is going on at each site, down to the individual agent level, it can determine exactly where the most qualified agent is located and available to handle the next transaction request. Usually, call-by-call routing is associated with network IVR processes so that the CRP knows exactly what the caller wants to do or who the caller actually is.

With the exception of ACD interflow above, the discussion of virtual call centers has focused on how intelligent network offerings provide increasing functionality. There is another approach available. Instead of duplicating entire centers, the alternative vision is to see agents as clients scattered around the extended enterprise. The functionality is extended through the existing telephone systems and the LAN/WAN private network. Among economic drivers advancing this vision is the projected growth in available IP bandwidth and the declining cost of high-speed, virtual private networks.

The alternative approach is defined and depends upon the available remoting options. In general, there are two remoting options. The first permits users to implement a remote cluster of agents anywhere a T-1 or E-1 circuit can reach. Think of this as taking a piece of your ACD system and placing it somewhere else. That piece doesn't have intelligence of its own. The second option permits an agent to be located anywhere, relying upon a high-speed Internet connection for application and contact center applications and a voice circuit for the delivery of telephone calls.

In a very real sense, users can create multisite, totally virtually contact centers using a single system with various remote agent options. What the user gives up is some disaster recovery flexibility but the economics might be compelling.

We can depict this kind of configuration as follows:

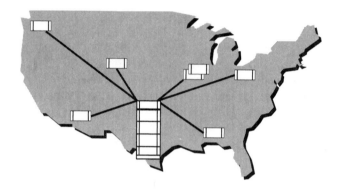

Figure 4-11. Remote Shelf Virtual System

A single switching system is established in a particular location. Instead of aggregating all the agents in one location, multiple small sites are established around the country. Each remote shelf is connected back to the central site with a simple T-1 span line. The remote shelf can support more than the expected 24 agents (in the case of T-1) through multiplexing. All the inbound trunks carrying callers arrive at the central site. This approach avoids the labor availability problems associated with very large call centers, retains time zone flexibility's and permits organizations to maintain local presence and preserve existing relationships.

Another configuration that is technically possible involves establishing a central system with combinations of local, remote shelves and individual remote agents. Most organizations have merely experimented with remote individual agents. While the technology supports the concept, management styles and insurance issues continue to hold back large-scale deployment of home-based agents.

The lessons already learned about running multiple call centers will certainly be applied to operating contact centers. There are many ways to operate in a decentralized environment. There is probably no single best answer for all organizations. It seems certain that we will be living and dealing with more highly distributed, yet well-connected, environments than might have been expected only a few short years ago. I suspect that contact centers will become increasingly virtual. As agent skill requirements soar, they will gain more leverage with respect to work environments. And, local and county governments will be promoting programs that reduce automobile commuting in efforts to improve the quality of the air we breathe.

E-Mail in the Contact Center

This is the first of the multimedia waves that are sweeping across contact centers around the world. E-mail has become the fastest-growing multimedia application. It seems the entire world has access to e-mail in one form or another.

Contact centers deal with a special subset of e-mail that is beginning to be referred to as Web-mail owing to the fact that visits to company Web sites provide both the means and the motive for the missive. Since by now we have all visited Web sites, everyone is aware that at the bottom of the page, usually in 6-point font, is the following statement, "Questions, comments: Send them to webmaster@xyz.com." Sometimes a generic department name, such as "sales" or "accounting" is used in place of the admonition to message the Webmaster. The point is that the message is directed to a function within the firm rather than to a person. This begs the question, who is responsible for answering these messages? Who will even access the inbox on a timely, recurring basis?

For many firms, the answer seems to be nobody. There are anecdotal stories aplenty regarding egregious mishandling of Web-mail messages. I have heard one story repeated by several different people. A business publication sent Web-mail messages to the manufacturers of personal computers. The message indicated that the firm was interested in purchasing *several thousand* desktop computers of a certain configuration and would the manufacturer please get back with a quote as soon as possible. The Web-mail messages went out. The publication waited for the responses to roll in. They waited an entire week before the first response arrived. Most manufacturers never responded to the Web-mail message! Might something like that already be happening in your company?

It's not just visits to Web sites that cause people to send e-mail messages to companies. Paul Anderson and Art Rosenberg are highly regarded in the contact center industry and co-authors of the book, *The Digital Call Center* (Doyle Publishing Company Inc. 1999). In that work, they identify the myriad of reasons why e-mail traffic is destined to be handled by call center personnel and why that traffic is rising dramatically. According to Anderson and Rosenberg, the reasons why people tend to send a message rather than initiating a real-time phone call include the following:

- They can't or don't want to wait for someone to assist them.
- They will use the context of web page information for the basis of their message inquiry or transaction.

- They need the convenience of 24/7 messaging access.
- They don't necessarily need to "discuss" anything about the information they want or the transaction requested.
- They might want to send information and data attachments first, before any interactive discussion is engaged in.
- They want a well-documented audit trail of the two-way messaging interchange.
- They want to eliminate the time, errors, and effort involved with transcribing detailed information during a live conversation.
- They don't have a required second telephone line for an immediate live callback while still connected to the Web.
- They want to direct their communication to a very specific group or individual that might not be readily accessible realtime.
- It's just more convenient and cheaper than a live connection.

So, it's clear why customers and prospects want to send e-mail messages to companies. But why should call centers become involved? Isn't handling e-mail fundamentally different from handling voice telephone calls?

Well, yes and no. Yes, handling e-mail is very different from handling a phone call. No, e-mail is a "faceless interaction," and that is something that call centers have learned how to do with efficiency and grace.

Happily, e-mail represents an interaction request that does not have to be dealt with in real time. For this, contact center managers should give thanks. It is rare that contact centers have deferrable work to deal with. Nearly everything else contact centers have to contend with occurs with real-time demands surrounding it. Not so, e-mail. Yes, there are response time issues connected with e-mail. I think most people understand that e-mails have to be answered within a reasonable time. But what, exactly, constitutes a reasonable time?

Reading a GartnerGroup report awhile ago, I was struck by a fact that had somehow eluded me. Namely, that 95% of e-mail messages are delivered within 5 minutes. Now I don't know about you, but before I read that fact I had the ill-informed impression that e-mail messages routinely took hours and hours to find their way into my inbox. And, this ill-formed impression shaped my response expectations. If the message wasn't received for at least 4 hours, then I couldn't reasonably expect a response until the next day. Now that I know better, my response expectations have moved up considerably.

The sense that I get from early practitioners is that 24 hours is the goal for e-mail response by some kind of unconscious default. There are companies that have the technologies and appropriately skilled people in place that would permit them to routinely answer e-mail messages within 2 hours of receipt but seem to have a "gentlemen's agreement" not to establish this as the service level goal. Other companies ought to thank their lucky stars that this is so. Raising the bar to this kind of service standard would cause serious problems for many organizations.

Because call centers have learned how to effectively and efficiently handle faceless interactions such as telephone calls, it seems certain that handling e-mails will become part of the task. Telephone calls, along with some other multimedia interactions, must be handled in real time and are initiated randomly. Try as we might, we cannot schedule telephone calls. But e-mail messages are different. The response time expectations surrounding them mean that this work can be deferred for short periods of time. When the demands for real-time interactions subside, contact center managers can turn to e-mail handling. This simplifies agent scheduling by reducing the need for part-time agents that work only during peak telephone periods.

To remain efficient, it seems natural to treat e-mail messages as if they were telephone calls. That is, e-mail messages represent work that needs to be queued, measured and managed. Moreover, since it seems clear that e-mail messages will be ultimately mixed with voice call handling, the same routing engine and the same reporting engine should be employed.

And that is what the vendors are bringing to market. There are generally two fundamental approaches regardless of the particular vendor. Many ACD vendors are adding functionality to their systems that effectively brings e-mail handling into the purview of the call processing and reporting routines. In effect, software accesses the e-mail inboxes periodically to determine if there are messages in need of attention. If there are messages present, the call processing system treats them as if they were just another phone call, albeit of a special call type. The call type designation typically points the system to a particular set of processing rules. Within these rules are specified the agents and agent groups eligible to handle an e-mail message. Exactly like voice calls, e-mail messages are presented to the agent and various data elements are recorded such as the following:
- The time the message spent in queue.
- The amount of time the message was being worked by the agent.
- Optionally, the breakdown of the overall work time into discrete steps, such as comprehending the message, researching the answer and writing the response.
- When the message response was sent.

The way the e-mail is "delivered" to the agent involves lots of arcane details but essentially the call processing logic causes the agent's voice connection to go into the "Unavailable" state while launching the appropriate e-mail client application software on the agent's desktop. The system collects performance data about that agent's work-metrics for that "call" type. This is a fairly painless addition of functionality for call processing systems with good skill routing and conditional processing capabilities.

The second fundamental approach to handling e-mail is absolutely necessary when volume grows to larger proportions than totally human resources can deal with effectively. Happily, call center users learned long ago that some kinds of telephone calls were of a simple, routine nature. Frequently, the agent merely looks up some information and reads data off their screen to the caller. Interactive voice response, discussed earlier, was invented to handle simple calls. The justification is economic. It is far less expensive to handle a call with an IVR than with an agent. A handful of software vendors have developed automated e-mail handling systems that mimic IVR. Even with limited deployment of e-mail processing in the contact center, it is evident that some e-mail messages are simple transactions.

Automated e-mail management systems use sophisticated logic routines, coupled with custom dictionaries in an attempt to decipher the content of each e-mail message. The following diagram illustrates the process:

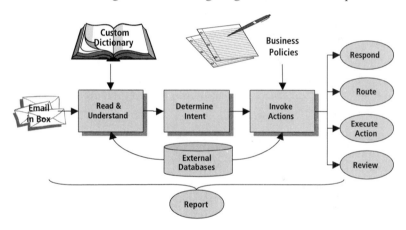

Figure 4-12. Automated E-Mail Management System

In effect, e-mail message contents are compared with words, phrases and acronyms that are unique and relevant to the enterprise. As the e-mail management system examines the content of a message, it is comparing the words and phrases in the message to the custom dictionary. If the system gets a high correlation between message content and custom dictionary, the system "knows" what the message is about. The system can then fetch a previously written, "canned" response that meets the needs of the sender and cause that response to be sent automatically. No human intervention required.

If the e-mail system gets a low correlation between message content and custom dictionary, the system may collect a number of potentially correct canned responses and forward the entire folder to a human agent. In this way, the agent can review the original message and quickly determine which, if any, of the canned responses is appropriate. If the system gets no matches at all, the original message is inserted in the human agent processing queue.

E-Mail Operational Insights

While there is much to learn about emerging expectations and service realities associated with multimedia transactions among vendors and users, there are already some tactics and strategies that seem to work well.

Because the response time expectations are so different from voice calls, a good e-mail processing step is to send an automated e-mail message back to the sender acknowledging receipt of the e-mail and specifying when, generally, the response can be expected. This step is important because many people are still uncomfortable with e-mail. In many ways, this is reminiscent of the early days of fax. Back then, when a fax was sent to a company it was frequently followed up with a quick phone call to ensure that fax was truly received. Sending an automatic acknowledgment to an e-mail sender will probably head off the phone call to the contact center asking if the e-mail message was received. On the other hand, after a company and a customer have engaged in several e-mail interactions, the customer may begin to perceive the automatic reply as a form of spam.

Some organizations appear to be embracing e-mail contact and justifying the cost of training and tools by projecting a reduction in voice calls. The early experience indicates a different reality. When you solicit e-mail and make it really easy to interact that way, e-mail contacts go up quickly. However, voice calling does not decrease. The rate of growth in voice calling decreases, sometimes substantially. But voice calling continues to grow in absolute terms after e-mail is successfully launched in the contact center.

The process described here implies that all agents will handle e-mail transactions. Because the nature of the question, the issue, the purpose of each e-mail message can vary from one to the next, it is extremely important that companies think about setting up e-mail templates for use with their Web sites. The point of the templates is to help sort the messages by nature of the content. By supplying a pull-down list of Web-mail Addresses (i.e., webmaster@xyz.com or sales@xyz.com), and a second pull-down list of Subject Lines, the firm has the opportunity to sort messages based on content, which facilitates skill matches. Typically, each different Subject Line would be classified as a different call type in the contact center transaction routing and reporting engine. You should also strongly consider providing a template for the Signature field of the message. You want to capture the sender's name, e-mail address and telephone number at a minimum. I have heard stories about companies receiving e-mail messages advising them to replace one item on an order with another. The only problem is that the message is simply signed, "Larry," and nobody can figure out who it really is.

The ultimate vision for many contact centers is the so-called "universal queue" operation. All transactions, regardless of the media type, enter a common queue. Each transaction has its value and priority to the enterprise. Agents handle a variety of transactions among a variety of media. Early experience indicates that not all agents are able to adapt to e-mail. Speaking well and writing well appear to be related only indirectly. Spelling is another matter entirely. Some agents love handling e-mail for the variety it brings to otherwise routine work experiences. A few agents are adept and quick enough to elegantly move from voice to e-mail and back to voice without effort. Others have difficulty shifting gears. The watchword is caution. If it were up to me, I think I would recruit some agents for a dedicated e-mail team and try to keep the application separate until I understood more about projecting the transaction volume and what the mix of transactions was likely to be before going forward. I'd also want to better understand the skill set required by e-mail transactions.

There is a second outcome from the universal queue operation that some people have trouble with. A single queue operation for mixed-media transactions implies that sometimes e-mail messages are more important than voice callers in queue. Unsettling though that thought might be, it's true. If an e-mail message from a top-tier customer is about to violate the response commitment and the voice calling service level has been acceptable for multiple time periods during the day, the e-mail message ought to be handled first. Of course, I would want some conditional tests performed by the system to make sure that overall voice service levels were acceptable and I wouldn't be imposing crazy, long queue times on the voice callers already in queue.

A final notion. There is no good reason why a proper response to an e-mail message cannot be in the form of a telephone call. In fact, I believe that companies that do this for some types of interactions can have a very positive impact upon the loyalty of selected customers. As marvelous as e-mail is, nothing beats the immediacy or warmth of a phone call.

Web Site Support

The newspapers, magazines and business journals all have similar articles. You must provide customer support for your Web site visitors. More and more people are disposed to doing transactions on the Web. The main reason they do not is that there is no provision for real-time customer support. Eventually, Web site support will become a contact center task. Why? For largely the same reasons that Web-mail is a contact center task. Contact centers are good at faceless interactions. You've got to do it. What are the available technologies?

In order of customer preference, from least preferable to most preferable, the Web site support technologies are:

- Call-Back Button
- Text Chat
- Assisted Browsing
- Voice over Internet Protocol (VoIP)
- Video over Internet Protocol (ViIP)

As we shall see, in spite of what you might have heard, mainstream, widely deployable solutions are not quite where we need them to be.

I have come to regard Web sites as something like electronic stores arrayed along an electronic street. As in real life, people window shop. Which is to say that they cruise down the street and simply give a passing glance at the shop window. Unless something catches the eye, the shopper is visually off to the next storefront window. That sounds suspiciously like Web surfing.

When we see a storefront window that looks interesting, we may linger at the window or decide to enter the store. If we do enter the store, and if you are like I am, you want the freedom to wander around the store without necessarily being pestered by the shop help. When I have a question, I like to have someone engage me quickly, answer my question, give me some guidance and then let me be. I think this is the way Web support ought to be approached, as well. Help should be available when needed but never overly obtrusive.

Call-Back Button

And so, that forms the problem with the first, easiest and least satisfying Web site support technology, call-back buttons. The usual implementation is to offer a "Contact Us" button on key Web pages where requests for support are most likely to be generated. When the Web site visitor clicks on the "Contact Us" button, a small window pops up with a call-back form. Typically, the name, telephone number and requested call-back time interval are requested. One of the choices is usually "immediate." Other choices are available by clicking radio buttons or by filling in a date and time field.

The vast majority of people surfing the Web from home have no second line into the home. Clicking the "immediate" call-back button request is the best choice in terms of timely service but there is no way the browser can stay on the Web site and receive a voice call-back. Voice call-backs after terminating the Web session are bound to be less effective if for no other reason than the moment is gone. There are some emerging technologies from the telephone companies that permit a Web surfer to have voice call waiting indications. That feature would help call-back button strategies a great deal.

Text Chat

Because call-back support schemes lose the moment, text chat is the next more preferable technology. In fashion similar to call-back, the Web visitor desiring support would click the "Contact Us" button and be presented with a pop-up text chat window. The software to enable the text chat window can be Java based and small enough to be downloaded to the Web visitor without any noticeable degradation in Web performance. With the text chat window open and floating above the Web page, the visitor and the agent can text dialog each other in real time. Better applications permit the agent to send pages to the visitor's Web browser.

Because text chat is a slower form of communication, some applications provide the agent with a library of frequently used phrases, sentences and entire paragraphs. Access to canned responses for frequently asked questions is important. Armed with these kinds of keystroke-saving tools, a skilled agent is thought to be able to handle multiple text chat sessions simultaneously. Evidence for this exists aplenty. If you have a young son or daughter who is into electronic messaging as available from America Online for example, then they can affirm that they and their peers are fully capable of handling as many as six chat sessions at the same time. If you are skeptical, as I am, that an agent can handle as many as six text chat sessions with quality and the appropriate style, at least take some comfort that these skills are seemingly being developed among younger people for free. Perhaps we will be able to leverage them successfully.

In general, I find text chat to be better than call-back but still far from a good solution to the problem of Web site support. Not everyone is comfortable typing with enough speed to avoid frustration. Not everyone is comfortable with removing all doubt that they are spelling-challenged by displaying their word art in real time for someone else to see. I believe that willingness to engage in text chat is related to age demographics. The older the Web visitor, the less likely that text chat will be regarded as a satisfying support mechanism.

Voice Over Internet Protocol

Call-backs fail because they lose the moment. Text chat seems too limiting and doesn't appeal to all Web site visitors. The next best technology is voice over Internet Protocol (VoIP). With this technology in place, the Web site visitor clicks on the "Contact Us" button. Typically, another Web page will float over the top of the main page that might contain the name of the agent and, perhaps, even a static picture. While still connected to the Web page, the visitor can speak with a live agent. The Web site visitor needs to have a multimedia-equipped personal computer. In practical terms, this means that they need a sound card and a microphone. In similar fashion, the agent is equipped with a multimedia personal computer, as well.

In operation, the agent and the Web visitor each see the same Web page on their respective browsers. The agent has access to information that identifies which other pages from the company's Web site that the visitor has already viewed. In this way the agent gets a sense of what the Web visitor has already done and where they have visited. In typical applications, the agent can "push" Web pages at the visitor. This means that the agent can cause the visitor's browser to display a new Web page. They can talk about the page. The visitor can cause the agent's browser to display a Web page. In our industry, this is referred to as "assisted browsing." In data terms, this is a peer-to-peer connection. In my view, this is the preferred way to support Web sites.

There is just one problem. We don't have enough bandwidth in the public Internet network or in the last one mile from the neighborhood junction box into our homes to make the technology work the way it needs to work.

People around the world have grown accustomed to high-fidelity conversations on the telephone. The fidelity is even getting much better on wireless calls. But when it comes to VoIP, latency and jitter matters. Jitter refers to the fact that packets will arrive at their destination out of order. We can accept more delay as we wait for the packets to arrive and do a sort or we can simply skip the out of order packet. Latency is a term that refers to the delay associated with a transmission. There is always a delay. Photons and electrons move at the speed of light, which has been repeatedly measured to be 186,000 miles per second. So, distance imposes a small delay. More important than distance is the time it takes various solid-state devices to do their respective jobs. When you pick up a telephone and speak to another person, the public-switched voice telephone network usually has less than a 20-millisecond total delay in transmission. This delay is caused by the codec that transforms your analog voice waves into a digitized stream of ones and zeros, the distance the stream has to travel, and the delay imposed by the codec at the other end.

The human brain is really good at compensating for the effects of transmission delay, up to a point—20 millisecond gaps are not noticed at all. It is this phenomenon that underlies all voice-compression schemes where voice signals are compressed to make more efficient use of available bandwidth without affecting clarity. It is not unusual to achieve compressions of 8:1 without noticeably compromising voice quality . But as delay, or latency, rises things go bad quickly. People begin to notice a delay when it reaches 50 milliseconds. Conversations begin to be disrupted when delays reach 100 milliseconds. When delays reach 250 milliseconds, the conversation is unintelligible for all practical purposes. As the delay increases, the parties begin to "talk over" each other. It is difficult to know when a party has stopped talking and is waiting for a response. People who remember when geosynchronous satellite voice circuits first came online will remember the frustrations associated with the relatively short delays imposed by that technology.

In the Internet, today, the typical multihop IP packet delay is as low as 150 milliseconds and is frequently as high as 500 milliseconds. This is the main reason why VoIP has not had a substantial impact upon contact center operations. VoIP is simply not ready for mass commercial deployment.

This is not to say that there are no VoIP implementations. Tightly control the delay and VoIP works well. The only place one can control latency is in a private network. So, VoIP technologies work well for internal users. You can employ VoIP technologies to facilitate remote agents. You can use VoIP to connect internal company users to agents in a help desk application. But using VoIP to interact with the masses as a replacement for costly 800 circuits remains a dream until quality-of-service issues associated with individual packets is resolved. Right now, the Internet treats all packets the same regardless of content. Thus, a packet that contains a piece of a fax transmission is treated no differently from a packet that contains a piece of a real time voice conversation. Clearly, we need IP networks to move the voice packet with more urgency than the fax packet. Until the Internet Service Providers furnish this kind of capability and we can run the numbers to ensure that a return on investment is achievable, VoIP won't reach its promise. When it does, however, nobody will ever be satisfied with call-backs or text chat again.

Video Over Internet Protocol

When all the bandwidth issues are resolved, the world will split into two camps. Those with video-enabled personal computers and those without. If there is enough bandwidth to carry on high-fidelity voice conversations over the Internet, there will likely be enough to have video connectivity, as well. How important is seeing? Suffice to say that humans are primarily visual creatures. So much information passes between people that is unspoken. Nuance and emotion are easily conveyed with looks and expressions. These visual cues are extremely important to effective communication between people. Surely, there is an important place for video interactions in contact centers.

This does raise some interesting issues. In the future, will agents need to be photogenic as well as skilled in more traditional areas? Clearly, the agent and the caller do not need to see each other constantly during the entire transaction. That would serve no point. When we are dealing with a store clerk, person to person, we don't spend every moment with our gaze fixed on the clerk. We look at other things. We listen. Occasionally, we glance at the person to pick up nonverbal cues and check that the interaction is still moving along. Perhaps video connections in contact centers will rely on avatars rather than real images. Avatar is a term given to an image that represents, or stands-in for, a person. Video game developers are moving this technology forward, as are firms, like Pixar, which are driving computer animation to new heights of realism. Just as many agents don't use their real names in call centers for privacy reasons, perhaps agents in multimedia contact centers will decide to use computer-animated avatars as their "virtual face."

Will we decide to reserve video interactions for only the best customers? As far into the future as anyone can see with any clarity, the video-enabled population will be relatively small, compared to mass-market populations. Because of the visual component, we should expect that video callers will develop preferences for and affiliations with particular agents. This might present some demanding transaction routing capabilities. If a video caller has to wait in queue, do we play a visual delay message? Do we offer a video caller the opportunity to leave a video message for us to review later?

Personally, I can't wait for video-enabled communications to arrive. Ever since I was a little kid watching reruns of old "Flash Gordon" serials from the 1930s, I've been fascinated by the notion of fully interacting across distance. My only regret is that the device we are likely to actually use in achieving this goal doesn't look nearly as cool as those old Flash Gordon contraptions with flashes of electricity, sparks and plenty of dials.

Desktop Re-Engineering

It is hard to imagine an agent in a contact center without some kind of computer system. While the general trend is towards client/server architecture, there are many dumb terminal/mainframe systems still in operation. Even within the client/server domain, there are factions promoting wildly different approaches that impact hardware, software and support. The point here is to recognize that there are many different kinds of computing environments. Thus, there are many, many different vendors offering tools that may or may not be workable in your own unique computing environment.

Having said that, you need to identify those vendors that can help as soon as possible. Because, the sorry state of the desktop in contemporary contact centers is holding back your performance.

Over the years, I have had the opportunity to visit hundreds of call centers. Many times I have been granted the opportunity to jack-in alongside an agent and listen to a few transactions, as long as the calls weren't personal in nature. It was the rare exception to the rule when I saw an agent interact with the screen in a natural, flowing, minimal navigation manner. Quite the contrary. All too often, the agent is required to launch multiple data access sessions. These multiple sessions are required because data necessary to deal with callers are scattered around the company in various databases. Beyond merely launching multiple sessions, the agent is frequently confronted with dense, cryptic screens, chock full of acronym headings and information.

The screens and the applications that the agents use to wrestle their way through a transaction are increasingly understood to be the central problem in creating effective and efficient customer contact centers. The screens cause eyestrain, stress and limit the productivity of even the best agents. The desktop disaster forms part of the reason why agent retention is so difficult for so many contact centers and why training classes keep getting longer without producing better-equipped agents.

There are a variety of approaches to consider. If budgets permit, firms can contemplate installing a completely new suite of application software from companies like Siebel, Vantive, Oracle and Quintus. These vendors offer complete software infrastructures that extend from the databases to the desktop applications. The applications generally cover sales, marketing and customer service across communication channels. The software might seem expensive and there are precious few instances where the software suite fits the individual company need without modifications and integration effort. This raises the cost of ownership substantially. Nevertheless, product suites from these and similar vendors are enjoying a hot marketplace as companies realize that buying software is less expensive than writing software, even with modification and integration expenses.

A second approach, one that is less expensive and disruptive, involves application development tools. There are many vendors who provide "tool kits" that permit trained personnel to design screens, access multiple databases and script the transaction.

In either approach, the desired outcome is to replace old application software and those dense, cryptic screens with easy-to-read, easy-to-use screens that are designed with workflow in mind. Workflow is a term that refers to how work is accomplished. Workflow is concerned with where data is stored, how transactions occur, the data required to conduct the transaction, the paths that transactions can take and the general flow of the work itself. Good workflow practices include concepts like:

- Straight-line navigation—Screens should flow from one to another without requiring agents to backtrack or jump to another screen within some other application.
- Just-right data presentation—The major problem with older screens is that developers were more concerned with system response times than workflow. So, whenever a mainframe database was accessed, an entire 1,920 characters of information was pulled and painted on the screen. The new thinking is to provide the agent with only the data necessary to conduct each small portion of the transaction. Perhaps we should refer to these as screen modules. Some screen modules might be used in multiple applications, such as a routine that verifies the identity of the customer before engaging in the particular matter.

• Access to 360 degree customer data—The major issue call centers will be dealing with as they morph into contact centers has to do with the fact that customers and prospects decide when and how to contact you from among a variety of channels. Each time an interaction takes place, the agent should have access to information that encapsulates previous transactions with that customer. In this way, the agent can avoid customer-displeasing behaviors linked to the firm's inability to break down the internal silos within itself.

Why Do We Need All This Technology?

For someone new to the industry, this looks like a formidable array of technology and the cost must be enormous. Can it be justified? Sure. Consider the following 5-year cost depiction:

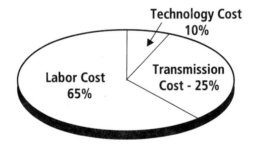

Figure 4-13. Relative Call Center Costs (Using In-WATS)

In most contact centers that use "800" numbers, this cost relationship is fairly accurate. The overwhelming cost is labor expense. Fully burdened labor easily costs the firm $50,000 annually for one moderately skilled and moderately paid agent. While the cost of transmission continues to decrease, in most contact centers it represents the next biggest expense. All the technology in the contact center rarely exceeds 10% of the total cost of the contact center.

The technology is used as a lever against the two large costs of labor and transmission. The Greek mathematician Archimedes is believed to have said that if he was given a lever big enough and a place to stand, he could move the earth. So it is for the contact center manager. The tools, costly though they may be, provide the lever and the place to stand so that the knowledgeable contact center manager can control the costs and deliver the revenues.

Chapter 5:
Contact Center
Management Challenges

If you've ever managed a contact center you will likely agree that it is a herculean task. Customers and prospects connect whenever the mood strikes them. There never seems to be enough resources. Everyone seems to be working hard but service level goals seem unrealizable. There is a low-level tension in the air and there are many reasons. This chapter identifies the difficulties and the dynamics that make operating a world-class contact center one of the more difficult challenges in business.

Six Failure-Causing Myths

After visiting hundreds of contact centers over the years and having spoken to even more contact center managers and supervisors, I have identified six commonly-held beliefs that tend to stack the deck against success in the contact center. These myths tend to afflict different responsibility levels with varying degrees of virulence.

The first, and most troublesome, myth is:

Myth #1
Contact Centers are Basically Pretty Simple Operations

If senior management holds this attitude, the chances of ever creating a truly world-class contact center diminish. This myth has some easily understood origins. The primary method by which people will interact with companies will remain the telephone for a long time. Telephones are common objects in our culture. They are everywhere and everyone knows how to use one. Because of this familiarity it is easy to assume a contact center is not a complex management task. Too often we hear senior management make remarks like:

"Establish a contact center? Well, get some phones. Get some people. What's the big deal?"

It *is* a big deal and complicated, as well. It's a big deal because contact centers interact with customers and prospects. In a typical contact center each agent will handle roughly 60 to 120 transactions per day. When you compare the number of interactions going on in a contact center with any other functional group in a business, it is clear that the contact center touches more customers. Each transaction, each interaction can have one of two outcomes: the customer is satisfied and remains a customer or the customer is not satisfied and prey to competitors' marketing efforts. What is at stake here is *quality* as perceived by the caller.

Quality is easily the most meaningful yardstick by which contact centers should be judged. Yet, quality measurements in contact centers are usually *inferred* rather than actually measured. It is inferred that there is quality in a contact center if the service level goal is being met and if too many callers aren't forced to abandon their call. Without a direct measurement process, there can be little doubt that managing a contact center for quality and productivity is complicated.

Managing a contact center is complicated because the contact center is an invisible world. All that management sees are the agents. Unfortunately, when you inspect a contact center visually, you cannot readily discern a poor center from an excellent center. A thought experiment will illustrate the point. Suppose that you run a "contact center" that does not use telephones but where the customers physically enter the agent room like in a bank lobby. As the manager of such a "contact center" you would be able to see:

• The number of customers waiting
• How long the wait-time is
• How many customers give up
• The number of return visits by individual customers
• The agents' courtesy and tone
• The average transaction time
• Each agents' ability to satisfy the customer
• Each agents' productivity

Seeing all these things would help you to form an impression of the overall efficiency of the center, to identify problem areas and to create plans for corrective action where appropriate. In a contact center you have none of these visual inputs. All you have are reports. Columns and rows of numbers. If you study them hard enough you might develop some kind of sense for what is going on in the center. This is the complicating factor.

Whereas the first myth is more the province of upper management, the second myth seems to afflict contact center managers and supervisors. The normal experience of people attempting to manage contact centers is that it is difficult. The second myth is like a beacon of hope:

Myth #2
The Right Technology will Manage the People

It is not surprising that contact center managers fail to get a firm grip on the center's reality from reports produced by the system. They soon become frustrated. It seems to require wading through reams of data with calculator and scratch paper handy. Amid all the technology it is easy to begin to believe that the reason this is so hard is that we don't have all the tools or the right kind of tools. What contact center managers would like is for the system to tell them what all the data means and what specific actions they need to take to produce desired results.

This myth is partially supported by a bias that exists in the industrialized parts of the world. We seem to have an elevated notion of the impact technology can have on all kinds of problems. If there is a problem, it is believed that there is or should be some technological quick fix that solves it. Compounding this is the fact that no contact center manager is going to tell his or her boss that the problem in the center is that the manager doesn't know exactly what to do. Rather, the contact center manager is likely to declare that if they only had the right tools, they could manage the center better. To a degree, there is truth in the myth. There is an appropriate level of technology for every contact center no matter the size or mission. As the skill of the management teams grows and as the size or importance of the contact center grows, the appropriate level of technology increases.

Support for this myth also comes from the idea that managing, interacting and motivating employees seems to be a disappearing art. Obviously, this has consequences in contact centers. They are people-intensive. Face-to-face exchanges between managers and agents can be difficult and emotional at times. Many managers seem to prefer an arm's-length involvement at best and no involvement at worst. This accounts for the desire that contact centers managers express in requests for new equipment regarding features that regulate agent behavior automatically or that deny behaviors thought nonproductive. This refers to features such as "make-available" where a supervisor can force an agent to take a call without talking to or physically encountering the agent. The belief that some managers don't like to interact with employees is reinforced by the growing use of voice mail and e-mail. Both communication methods impose time and space separation. It seems that people prefer them because there is no face-to-face interaction. This is lethal in the contact center for reasons identified in Chapter 6.

The third contact center myth is somewhat related to the second:

Myth #3
The Right Technology will Produce High Productivity

This myth is the result of hope over experience. If our contact center is not performing to expectations, we can look to three reasons; the agents are not performing, the system lacks required capabilities or the manager is struggling. Vendor salespeople selfservingly suggest that the problem always lies in the existing equipment.

Over the years, the equipment vendors have engaged in a feature war. First, it was longest available agent routing over uniform call distribution. Then, it was specialized agent instruments. Next, was call routing mechanisms. The feature battles then changed to lots of printed reports. The battle waged over historical reports. Next, it was graphical reports. For awhile it was ISDN. Then, it was ANI. It shifted to skills-based routing. Lately, we get heavy doses of customer relationship management bromides and exhortations to jump into the deep end of multimedia transaction processing in the media-neutral center. The strong implication is always that if you do not have this feature or that capability, you can not operate a truly successful contact center. The goal will always elude you.

That is not to say that you don't need technology to succeed. But features alone can never ensure success. Why? *Agents* interact with customers, features do not.

Myths 2 and 3 are related and supporting them is the story a bank customer service manager encountered several years ago. She was responsible for a large customer service operation that used a popular PBX-based ACD. The center was stuck at a performance plateau and she became convinced that lack of more sophisticated technology was the problem. She felt certain that better reporting coupled with better call routing capabilities would boost productivity. She convinced senior management to finance acquisition of a new system. Immediately after the new system was installed, productivity improved by about 10%. The problem was that the performance began to drop off during the next couple of months. Six months after the new system was installed, the performance of the center was exactly where it was when the old system was there. And, the trend-lines were all headed downward.

This contact center manager was the victim of Myths 2 and 3. Initially, it looked as if the new "tools" had indeed produced a productivity improvement. But after some time, the performance decreased to previous levels. Fortunately, she recognized what was happening and implemented a quality and productivity improvement program aimed at the agents that delivered more persistent improvements in performance.

This kind of thing happens all the time. The initial improvement in performance is little more than the "Hawthorn Effect." This phenomenon was first observed and identified more than half a century ago at the Western Electric Hawthorn Works in a suburb of Chicago.

As the now-famous story goes, this plant's efficiency experts were studying a particular assembly line. The stations on this line involved close wiring work. They decided to see if improved lighting on the assembly line would have any impact upon productivity and quality. They installed higher wattage bulbs and measured performance. Both productivity and quality measures showed improvement. One of the experts decided to continue the experiment in order to learn if performance improvements would continue to improve as lighting became stronger. The efficiency team was impressed with what appeared to be proof that the more lighting the factory provided the greater was the workers output. Quite whimsically, after months of raising lighting levels and measuring performance they decided to reduce the lighting levels. They expected to see performance decline. Surprise! Performance improved some more.

The bottom line on the Hawthorn Effect is that if you fiddle around with their environment, workers performance will improve—just because you got involved and showed some interest. It almost doesn't matter what you do. Of course, there are limits to performance in any task. And, you can't make the Hawthorn Effect work over long periods of time by continuing to fiddle. The moral of this story is to be cautious about technology's ability to increase productivity by itself. Technology does not complete transactions with the exceptions of interactive voice response and self-help Web sites.

A source of much frustration is the fourth myth:

Myth #4
The Quality of Customer Handling
cannot be Measured or Quantified

We mentioned earlier that the vast majority of contact centers deal exclusively in the delivery of customer service. A revenue-generating contact center can always be measured by the dollars coming in versus the expense of the operation. Such a straightforward measure does not come readily to mind for the customer service center. Quality has increasingly become a desirable yardstick for many kinds of business-customer interactions. In general, business has come to recognize that quality needs to be packaged with every transaction, interaction and operation in order to survive. For contact center managers, the problem is: How to define and measure quality?

This is *not* a trivial problem. The way an exchange between two people is perceived by the parties is complex and colored by emotion. Since feelings are involved, the quantification of quality must include some kind of judgment. But who decides? What judgment is unbiased? Quality may be defined as *customer satisfaction*. This rule would assign high scores if the customer finished the transaction feeling good and their needs had been understood and met. But suppose that you operate a bank customer service center and a customer calls in complaining about a nonsufficient funds fee that appears on their checking statement. If it is the bank's standard policy to enforce nonsufficient funds penalties, the agent has no latitude. In this case, the caller will not feel good about the transaction. If asked by a third party, the customer will likely have bad things to say about the bank. Are you forced to score such a call as lacking in quality because of bank policy? How is that a reflection of the agent's skill and knowledge?

What can be concluded is that existing approximations of quality in a contact center—statistics about queue length, service levels and others—are too coarse to be particularly useful. They are global and nonspecific. In the next chapter, is a detailed quality measuring process that relies upon the adherence of the contact center to written policies and procedures.

The following contact center myth has surprising acceptance among experienced agents, as well as supervisors:

Myth #5
You can have High Productivity or High Quality,
but not both!

The lament of contact center supervisors is often heard in terms similar to the following:

"If I stress quality, productivity goes down. If I stress productivity, quality goes down. It's a Catch-22 situation."

What they are referring to is the result of agents' perceptions concerning what management means by productivity and quality in the first place. It is our finding that when contact center management stresses quality, agents interpret the request in the following terms:
  • Slow down the conversations
  • Take more time with each customer
  • Be "friendly" and chat a bit

If they behave this way, it is certain that the productivity of the contact center will decrease in numerical terms. That might not be a bad thing. So many contact centers seem to have placed themselves on a treadmill, portraying themselves as if they were call factories. Similarly, if contact center management stresses productivity, agents interpret the request in the following terms:
  • Speed up
  • Get through each call quickly
  • Stick to business and finish, no pleasantries

If agents behave this way, it is likely that some callers will feel rushed and may perceive the experience as being cold and unsatisfying. At a minimum, errors will begin to creep into the operation.

It doesn't have to be this way. In a contact center with good quality measuring mechanisms, the data revealed that there was no direct correlation between either quality and talk-time or productivity. There were agents in the center that had high quality and short talk times, as well as low quality and long talk times. The irony could be that in order to have a world-class contact center you must have high quality and high productivity. The management chapter shows how both can be achieved.

The last of our troublesome myths is:

Myth #6
Agent Skills Grow with Time on the Job

A tourist is walking through Manhattan and stops a stranger on the street to ask how to get to Carnegie Hall. The stranger replies, "Practice, practice." An apocryphal story, no doubt. Yet, this belief permeates life. We all believe that if we practice, we will get better at the task. This notion is so widely held that we no longer even question its applicability in different situations.

This was touched on earlier. A contact center is unique because it is an invisible world. This impacts the agents, as well as management. After an agent goes through whatever training program is available, the nature of the work in the contact center usually precludes any improvement by virtue of repetition. Instead of improving, agents develop habits and automatic responses to situations that present themselves. Agents repeat these habits indefinitely because they are never exposed to another approach. Telephone calls are relatively private exchanges between people. Agents are almost never offered an opportunity to hear another agent handle callers and seldom even get a chance to hear themselves!

There is no such thing as on-the-job training for agents in contact centers because their work is isolated and they cannot learn from each other. The isolation of agents is the source of more management problems that most people realize. There is much more to say about this in the management chapter.

Issues and Problems

The things that vex contact center managers and supervisors can easily be listed. These concerns have been identified in various seminars and heads always nod in agreement. A good generic list of problems would include:
- Agent attrition rate is too high
- Differences in motivation: New Hires vs. Oldtimers
- How to balance staff to call load
- How to deal with surges in traffic
- What statistic should I manage
- How to provide coverage during breaks and lunches
- How to keep agents on the phone
- How to properly evaluate performance
- How to measure and manage quality

- How to provide better, more cost-effective training
- How to calculate cost per call
- How to get real value from all those ACD reports
- Where can I find trainable people willing to be agents

This list is interesting for several reasons. One, the majority of items have to do with contact center managers wanting to know how to accomplish a particular task. So, the state of the art of contact center management has moved far past identifying problem areas. The problems are known. It is the workable solutions that elude us. Second, most of the issues and problems have to do with *people*, not technology. This implies that technology's role is understood and used appropriately for the most part. Making the mix of technology and people work efficiently appears to be among the problems. It is as if an alien race had descended to earth and bestowed advanced technological tools on us but left without giving complete instructions on their use.

The key reasons why contact centers are difficult to run successfully has to do with the following three observations:
- Contact centers are unique blends of people and technology.
- There are lots of variables that affect performance.
- The variables are constantly changing.

It would be difficult to identify another area in companies where high technology and people come together in such numbers.

One way to internalize the idea that contact centers are difficult to manage is to compare the task of running an inbound center with that of running an outbound center. If the task is to organize an outbound telemarketing center and the goal is to call 300 people on a list within one hour to deliver a particular message, our planning task is straightforward enough to be accomplished with a calculator. If we know that the message takes 3 minutes to deliver, we can quickly estimate that an average telemarketer can deliver about 17 messages per hour. It is a simple matter of division to determine how many telemarketers will be needed on the phone in order to reach 300 people in one hour. Roughly speaking, we will require about 18 telemarketers.

Now contrast this simple exercise with a similar mission statement for the inbound contact center manager:

"Hello, Mr. Contact Center Manager. I want your people to handle our incoming calls tomorrow from 10:00 AM to 11:00 AM. The center expects to receive 300 calls, but that's only an estimate. There could be more or less calls. Each call is expected to take about 3 minutes. But, some will be longer and others will be shorter. We can't tell you exactly how the calls will arrive during the hour, but all 300 calls will arrive. One more thing. The boss wants at least 80% of these calls answered within 20 seconds of arrival, and nobody should get a busy signal. Good luck!"

The tasks are wildly different owing to the control, or lack thereof, over complicating variables.

Contact Center Dynamics

Nothing illustrates the problem of complicating variables better than a case study of a hypothetical contact center using Erlang C and Erlang B statistical tables. The assumptions for our hypothetical contact center are:

Average talk time = 180 seconds
Average after-call work time = 30 seconds
Calls in a half-hour = 250
Service Level objective = 20 seconds

Reps	P(0)	ASA	Dlydly	Svc Lvl	Occ	Trk Load
30	82.8%	208.7	252.0	23.5%	97%	54.0
31	65.2%	74.7	114.5	45.2%	94%	35.4
32	50.7%	37.6	74.1	61.3%	91%	30.2
33	38.8%	21.3	54.8	73.0%	88%	28.0
34	29.3%	12.7	43.4	81.5%	86%	26.8
35	21.8%	7.8	36.0	87.5%	83%	26.1
36	15.9%	4.9	30.7	91.7%	81%	25.7
37	11.4%	3.1	26.8	94.6%	79%	25.4
38	8.1%	1.9	23.8	96.5%	77%	25.3
39	5.6%	1.2	21.4	97.8%	75%	25.2
40	3.8%	0.7	19.4	98.6%	73%	25.1
41	2.6%	0.3	16.4	99.5%	69%	25.0

I've seen this and similar charts used by people around the world. There is nothing proprietary about Erlang statistical tables, but the format of this chart was very likely created by Gordon MacPherson and Brad Cleveland of Incoming Calls Management Institute.

Before we start drawing the interesting inferences from this table of data, we should identify the column headings. They are as follows:

Reps—the number of staffed positions in our hypothetical contact center.

P(0)—the probability that a random caller entering our contact center will experience a delay before human answer.

ASA—an acronym for average speed of answer. This is the mathematical average delay before answer for all callers entering the center expressed in seconds.

Dlydly—the average delay expressed in seconds for callers who actually experience a delay. This figure differs from ASA in that ASA also counts callers who get answered immediately.

Svc Lvl—the service level expression or the percent of callers who get answered within the desired goal of 20 seconds.

Occ—the percentage of time that agents are either talking to callers or doing legitimate after-call work.

Trk Load—the number of hours of call traffic that the center's trunks will have to carry given the staffing.

The observations and implications that can be drawn from the table of values represents an "advanced degree" in contact center dynamics. The first observation is that *bad service costs money*. Notice that as staffing increases from 30 positions to 41 that the amount of traffic that must be carried decreases from 54 hours to 25 hours. If the contact center relies upon "800" service to bring in callers, this difference in traffic has a significant cost. Not only is real money paid to the interexchange carrier providing the "800" service, but more trunk ports on the switching system must be purchased to accommodate the extra trunks. These real-dollar expenditures can be used to hire more agents. To a degree, you can provide better service levels for free just by trading trunk costs for agent costs.

An observation that must be made is that *while there is no useful industry standard level of service* that contact centers should provide, *most centers seem to use a service level goal of 80% calls answered in 20 seconds or less.* Often, contact center managers ask what their service level goal should be. The reply depends upon what the company is willing to afford and/or what their competition is willing to afford. It is suggested that contact center managers routinely call into their own centers at random times of the day and measure answer delay. Managers should also call competitors' contact centers and perform the same measure. One contact center manager did this very successfully. She monitored answer times at four competitors and arrayed the data in a simple chart that she appended to her request for additional budget. She got it.

Scanning the table's service level column reveals that staffing 34 positions will provide a service level of 81.5%. A stunning observation is that *the difference between good service and poor service can be just a few staffed positions.* Examine what happens when just three agents get up and leave their positions. The staffing drops from 34 to 31 which represents a 10% decrease. The service level plummets from 81.5% to a dismal 45.2%. Or, consider the impact on average speed of answer. When the three agents leave their positions, average speed of answer explodes from 12.7 seconds to 74.7 seconds. It seems unfair that contact center dynamics should be so nonlinear.

Another observation that must be made here has to do with average speed of answer. *Managing by average speed of answer is dangerous* because it can be misleading. In fact, the whole mathematical concept of average is poorly understood by most of us. Averages are fictitious. They represent nothing real. Examine the 33 staffed positions row of data. The average speed of answer is projected to be 21.3 seconds. That doesn't sound terribly poor, does it? The rest of the data, however, makes it clear that the service may, indeed, be perceived as poor. More than one-third of the callers will experience a delay before answer. On average, these callers experience a delay of slightly less than one minute on hold! Some of these callers will be forced to wait much longer.

Averages are very misleading and you can prove it for yourself. Imagine that you have two buckets of water. One bucket holds ice water while the other holds boiling water. If you place one foot into each bucket of water, on average you will feel comfortable. Or will you?

Notice the occupancy column. As the staffing and service level increases the occupancy of the agents decreases. This is dangerous because of a management philosophy that has gained popularity of late. This new philosophy is known as "managing by wandering around." Senior executives are urged to get out of their offices and simply walk around the company. By observing what is going on, it is felt, they will be more in touch with what is happening, will be better positioned to identify problems areas and can propose corrective actions without requiring much study. An uninformed senior manager could walk into a contact center that is delivering excellent service and determine that the center must be overstaffed because some agents appear to be unoccupied.

It is an immutable law of contact centers that *service level and occupancy are inversely related*. That is, good service is always linked with lower occupancy while poor service is always linked with higher occupancy. Why should this be so? The only way agents can have low occupancy is when they have finished a call, make themselves available to take another call and discover that no callers are waiting! No callers waiting means good service. Conversely, if an agent completes a call, becomes available and is immediately connected to another caller; that agent will have high occupancy. If callers are always waiting so that the agents are always immediately connected to another caller, by definition that center is always imposing queues and likely offering poor service. You can never get good service and high occupancy unless you have some deferrable work that can be easily engaged and disengaged at will. Happily, e-mail processing might be just the kind of work to add to contact centers with lower occupancy.

One of the more subtle implications of the data has to do with callers waiting in queue. By examining the row of data associated with 34 staffed positions (our so-called ideal staffing), notice that the probability of a random caller encountering a delay is 29.3%. Said another way, nearly one out of three callers will experience a delay. Moreover, the average delay for these delayed callers will be 43.4 seconds. Although not portrayed in the data table above, the Erlang function predicts that a few callers will wait (if they are willing) nearly 3 minutes before connecting with an agent. It seems to be particularly the case with executives that their expectation is that nobody will have to wait. Or, that the wait time will be very minimal.

It happens many times. An executive walks into the contact center and glances at the supervisor screen. The executive sees that there are callers in queue and the longest waiting call has aged beyond 45 seconds. This is surely poor service, the executive thinks. Wrong! In contact centers it is normal for some callers to wait. In well-run contact centers, *some callers always wait*. In fact, contact centers would not be affordable by anyone if the rule was that no callers wait on hold. The art of contact center science is: (1) *making sure valuable customers get good service, and* (2) *preventing too many callers from waiting too long*.

One of the last observations of the case data is perhaps the scariest. It has already been shown what happens when just 10% of the staff gets up and leaves their positions. Service plummets. The other shoe dropping occurs when any of the variables whose values are fixed in the case assumptions changes by just 10%, service plummets. Imagine that instead of 250 call arrivals in a half-hour that we get 10% more. Our center has to process 275 calls. Just 25 more calls spread over 30 minutes. It doesn't seem rational that a mere 25 additional calls would impact the service level so dramatically. Likewise, if the average talk time increases by 10% or the average after-call work time increases by 10% the center's performance will tumble. *Minor variations in any of the variables produce exaggerated outcomes in service level*. You can illustrate this for yourself with the following word picture: Contact centers operate on the edge of a cliff.

Why It's Difficult

The dynamics surrounding a contact center are volatile. Small changes in variables produce big changes in service level. Some myths have been identified that tend to stack the deck against successful contact center management. Issues and problems that seem to afflict all contact center managers are fairly easy to compile. It's time to move from the general to more specific sources of difficulty.

The single source for most of the difficulty associated with running a successful contact center is that *call arrivals are predictable occurrences of random events*. That statement needs some contemplation and elucidation.

Consider the behavior of a single caller. After recognizing a need to do some telephone transaction with a firm, the actual telephone call placement is totally random. Nobody, not even the caller, can predict exactly when the call will be placed. It is largely a matter of available time, priority and degree of motivation. Multiply the single caller by hundreds and even thousands and you begin to get a feel for the randomness of the call attempts. It is true that over time, a contact center will begin to see patterns of call arrivals. Depending upon the nature of the business, a particular contact center might experience higher call volumes on Monday than on Tuesday. Given enough experience, the center manager might even be able to predict with some accuracy the total number of call attempts that will arrive at the contact center. However, it is one thing to say that 250 call arrivals are expected in the half-hour between 9:00 A.M. and 9:30 A.M., and an entirely different thing to predict how the calls will actually arrive during the half-hour! Stated another way, there are an overwhelming number of ways that 250 call arrivals can be realized in a half-hour. The best arrival pattern from the contact center manager's perspective would be a steady, even rate, minute by minute. Unfortunately, that is the least likely arrival pattern that can be realized.

The effect of randomness on call arrival patterns causes the calls to arrive in bunch. Viewing a single half-hour of call arrivals in a very detailed, granular fashion often reveals the following kind of pattern depicted in figure 5-1:

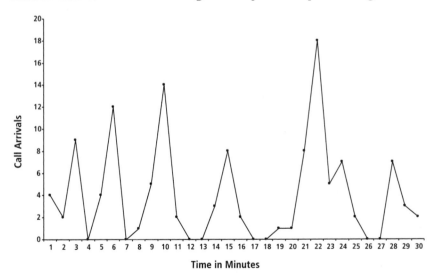

Figure 5-1. 120 Random Call Arrivals in 30 Minutes

The microbursts of call arrivals create short-term perturbations in the contact center dynamics similar to what was detailed in the case study earlier in this section. This accounts for the fact that even if you forecast call arrivals with high accuracy and staff appropriately for that call volume, the center can experience some periods where the number of callers in queue soars and the age of the oldest waiting caller is beyond toleration.

Another major source of difficulty has to do with the fact that *agents are not machines*. Many would suppose that this doesn't need to be pointed out but just as caller behavior is random, an agent's behavior is also random, within some limits. This is another aspect of the problem with averages. An agent report might indicate that a particular agent handles 14 calls per hour on average but that in no way means that, for a particular hour, the agent will in fact handle 14 calls. Agent performance expressed as an average is actually a probability. Many people have some difficulty understanding the mathematics of probability.

A familiar example can shed some light on this. Consider a coin toss. There are two possible outcomes, heads or tails. If the coin is fair we can say that the probability of a head is 50% and the probability of a tail is 50%. So far, everything seems pretty straightforward. Now suppose that the coin is tossed one hundred times. The mathematics of probability state that there is a very, very small chance of getting exactly 50 heads and 50 tails. There is a very high chance of getting somewhere between 40 and 60 heads. We can predict with confidence that there will be some number of heads between 40 and 60 but we can't predict with any confidence exactly how many actual heads will be tossed. Transpose this to agent performance and consider the impact of being wrong by as little as 10%, as exemplified in the case study. It's easy to be "wrong" enough on performance in some short period of the day to cause operating statistics to look terrible.

Yet another source of difficulty is that *transactions times vary through the day*. The degree of variance can be surprising. Part of this is explainable by recognizing that agents get fatigued as the shift wears on. Agents usually are the crispest early in the shift. Even the application of adequate breaks and lunches cannot prevent what can be called the "slump factor." But sometimes, external factors will cause transactions times to vary. In one case, the contact center was troubled by a recurring increase in transaction time late in the afternoon. The management of the center tried rearranging breaks. They tried altering the mix of experienced and new agents signed on in the afternoon. Nothing seemed to have any impact on the increase in transaction time. In frustration, they even began to tinker with the environment thinking that perhaps afternoon sun was creating glare on the screens.

Quite by accident, months later the management discovered the source of their problem. It seems that every afternoon as the first data processing shift drew to a close it was common practice for several large batch-processing jobs to be started up on the mainframe computer. These large jobs consumed computer resource. The very same computer drove the agents' terminals. Hence, when the afternoon batch jobs were fired up the terminal response time lengthened. This increase in terminal response time caused the transaction time to increase. External events can have serious second-order effects upon contact centers.

Even if the contact center manager has solutions to the problems discussed above, she would be faced with *a fundamental inability to accomplish precision staffing*. If the call arrival pattern could be identified with a high degree of accuracy and if the complicating changes in variables did not occur, the manager would seek to minimize the labor expense of the agent force by scheduling as closely as possible to the call requirement. This can be depicted in the following graph:

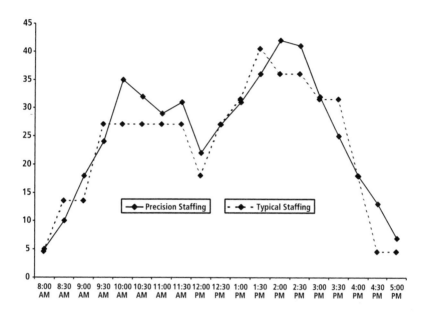

Figure 5-2. Call Arrival Pattern vs. Staffing Levels

This implies that the contact center manager has access to a lot of part-time agents. She would schedule some of the part-time people to help cover peak periods of traffic. It doesn't help that the typical contact center experiences two peak periods of traffic each day; one in the morning and one in the afternoon. This means that the manager would need to find agents willing to work very short hours and suffer two commutes a day. There aren't many agents willing to work such short hours combined with unacceptable shift patterns. Some contact centers approximate this by loaning agents to other departments when the calls diminish in numbers. But that strategy really does not reduce the labor expense of the firm, it just reallocates the expense among multiple cost centers. The better solution would be to acquire home agent capability.

The Contact Center Challenge

Building a world-class contact center is difficult. Being a successful contact center manager is exactly like tossing a coin in the air and having the coin land precisely on its edge. If it lands heads up, you've spent too much on agent labor (overstaff). If it lands tails up, you've understaffed and provided poor service with attendant costs in goodwill and/or revenue. The coin must land on its edge. Moreover, the coin must be tossed every half-hour of every day!

Chapter 6:
A Management Process for Productivity and Quality

If there are several hundred thousand contact centers in the world, it is likely that there are at least as many different management techniques being practiced. What makes this so unusual is that contact centers have more in common with each other than most would admit. Yes, the applications are different. Yes, the industries are different. Yes, the equipment is varied. Even so, all contact centers deal in phone calls, e-mail, Web site support, service levels, transaction times and transaction arrival patterns. This makes it all the more surprising that contact center managers seemingly must discover for themselves what data to track and how to respond.

Over the years, in visits to hundreds of contact centers it has been noticed that the successful centers share certain things in common, as do struggling centers. After thinking about what had been seen and all the ideas others had generated, a management process emerges that can be referred to as a Quality/Productivity System. While this process definitely produces results, it takes *effort and time*. Before detailing the process, it is beneficial to walk through some of the insights and philosophies that preceded the synthesis of the process.

Five Contact Center Realities

One of the first clues that many of the performance problems in contact centers might be solved with a process instead of a technology fix emerged as a result of consulting work. A consultant rarely gets hired to analyze a center that is meeting expectations. No, a consultant gets hired to help centers in trouble. A useful technique is to develop a statistical view via the reports. Then interviews are conducted to give the statistics a "face." The statistics tell what has happened; the interviews begin to reveal why and even suggest what to do next.

A realization came over time that there are *five dynamics* or realities that seem to exist for all contact centers. They are not obvious. If you are not aware of them, they can work against you and hurt center performance. If you understand them and make them part of your management process, the center can achieve goals with less effort.

Since a contact center's performance is directly affected by the performance of the individual agents, agent productivity is often analyzed. The first contact center reality is:

The performance variation of experienced agents is usually huge and the cause is not simply lack of motivation.

When all the experienced agents are collected into a group and some normalizing of the data is performed (explained later in this chapter), there is often a difference of three to one or more in contacts handled. Be careful to avoid daily data owing to the random nature of call allocation. Always look at performance data for at least five to ten days. Over this time frame, the random nature of call allocation will work itself out among the agents.

The huge productivity difference among experienced, tenured agents does not happen because some agents have bad attitudes. Agents don't learn better behaviors by doing the job and they don't have the benefit of observing other agents doing the job. As a result, acquired habits and patterns develop into job behaviors that persist over time. These habits and patterns limit performance in an individual and collectively limit performance in the center.

The existence of this dynamic accounts for the negative results most contact center managers get when they attempt to exhort the agents to higher performance levels. Contests, instrument displays, wallboards and flashing lights are typically employed to inform and motivate agents to higher productivity. The underlying idea is that the agents can do better if only they would try harder. All these performance-enhancing techniques, if they produce any improvement at all, tend to be effective for only a short time, after which the agents and the center settle back into normal performance.

The second dynamic observed deals with management reporting systems used in contact centers.

The many ACD management reports have very little utility unless they are viewed in a "knowledgeable" fashion.

There are many different contact center vendors, each with their own data presentation. Each reporting system provides essentially the same data although the manner and style of presentation are different. Nearly all the good reporting systems feature a large variety of reports containing columns and rows of numbers. Happily, some of the numeric data has been arrayed into graphic displays. The typical contact center manager is literally drowning in a sea of data. It is like trying to get a drink of water from a fire hydrant. What is needed are a few key metrics that can be easily tracked. But which metrics?

The third and fourth dynamics have to do with quality. In an earlier section quality was discussed as one of the keys to enterprise success. A persistent problem in the contact center has to do with the fact that quality has always been inferred rather than measured. Managers infer good quality when the service level target is realized or when the abandon rate is low. Of course, these are useful inferences but they are global and lack precision. The third dynamic is:

The quality of customer handling can be measured and managed at an individual agent level.

This will be detailed later in this chapter. For now, there are some additional observations about quality. Quality in a contact center is a very soft concept. It is judgmental. It is subjective. Quality is a lot like art. There is a quote attributed to a former Supreme Court member to the effect that art and pornography may resist precise definition but are always recognized when it is seen. Quality is just like that. We might not be able to precisely define what constitutes quality in a contact center but we know it when we encounter it.

The fourth dynamic is a powerful lesson for many agents. Noted earlier was that one of the problems facing contact center managers had to do with agent behaviors arising from stressing first productivity and then quality. Agents perceive management requests for attention to quality as a request for the agent to be "friendly" and "chat" with callers a bit before moving to business. This is natural. It is a blending of personal phone behaviors with business phone behaviors. The surprising fourth dynamic is:

The quality perceived by callers has little practical relationship to the length of the conversation.

While there are exceptions to every rule, this dynamic is provable. In contact centers that have implemented quality measurement processes, quality scores were plotted against average talk time. If there was a relationship between quality and length of conversation, a line could be drawn through the data points. Depicted here is just such a graph from an actual contact center.

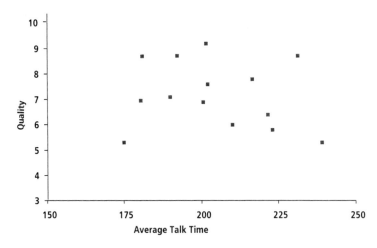

Figure 6-1. Quality Score vs. Average Talk Time

Instead, no relationship between the variables can be discerned. There are agents providing high quality and short transaction times. There are agents providing low quality with longer transaction times. The lack of a mathematical relationship is an important insight that must be shared and internalized by agents for the contact center to become truly successful. The lack of a relationship between quality and talk time means that business phone calls operate under a different set of rules than personal calls. It must be the case that most business callers value efficiency over pleasantries.

The fifth and final dynamic is no great surprise but is often overlooked for the powerful influence it exerts in the contact center.

The average customer wait time (the queue) is extremely sensitive to the match between the incoming call load and the number of agents available on the phones.

This is mentioned in an earlier section when we looked at the Erlang case study. This dynamic can't be emphasized enough. Consider that service levels are a lot like academic grade-point averages. One single bad grade limits your overall grade-point average in spite of the rest of the scores. One bad half-hour in the morning and another in the afternoon is all it takes to have a poor service level for the day. You can't catch up. Another way of seeing this dynamic is represented in the following table:

Calls in 30 Min.	% from Baseline	Prob. of Delay	ASA In Sec.	DlyDly In Sec.	Service Level %	Agent Occ.	Over/ Under Staff
288	+15%	92.0%	482.9	525.0	11.5%	99%	+4
275	+10%	65.3%	71.5	109.6	45.6%	94%	+3
263	+ 5%	45.6%	28.9	63.3	66.8%	90%	+2
250	Baseline	29.3%	12.7	43.4	81.5%	86%	34 Staff
238	- 5%	18.4%	6.2	33.7	89.8%	82%	-1
225	-10%	10.3%	2.8	27.1	95.1%	77%	-3
213	-15%	5.6%	1.3	23	97.7%	73%	-4

Table 6-2: Performance Impact of Minor Variations in Call Arrival Rate

This table is related to the Erlang-derived chart presented earlier. The intent of the chart is to show the impact center performance related to changes in the number of calls arriving into the hypothetical contact center defined in Chapter 5. The baseline is 250 call arrivals in 30 minutes. If we staff at 34 positions, from the chart in Chapter 5, we expect to answer 81.5% of the calls within 20 seconds of arrival and the average speed of answer for all callers will be 12.7 seconds. The chart shows what happens to the calculated performance metrics when the number of calls arriving in 30 minutes fluctuates in 5% increments.

As the table indicates, relatively minor changes in call arrival rate produce huge swings in average speed of answer and service level. The last column shows how many additional agents are needed to maintain service levels in the case of rising call arrival rates and how many surplus agents are available for other things during declining call arrival rates. Note that 15% swings in call arrival rates are fairly routine. Contact centers seem to operate on the edge of a service level cliff.

These dynamics or realities that confront contact center managers led to a list of six principles that are key to building a world-class contact center.

Six Principles Leading to World-Class Contact Centers

Before discussing the management process, it is useful to identify the underlying principles so that variations on this approach can be considered and created. The six principles are:

1. The contact center's management infrastructure must be complete.
2. The contact center's management must maintain two basic balances.
3. Management must manage down to an individual agent level.
4. Performance must be made visible at an individual agent level.

5. The center must be managed in real time and in either 15- or 30-minute intervals.

6. The primary role of supervisors is to make low performing agents become more productive. A close secondary responsibility is to manage time—for themselves and their agents.

The following pages will explain what each point implies and expand the concepts.

Infrastructure of the Contact Center

This term, when applied to the contact center, has several meanings. First, it is impossible to create a world-class contact center with inadequate equipment. Earlier you were cautioned against falling prey to a contact center myth that seductively suggests the proper technology will both manage the agents and ensure high productivity. However, to be truly successful and economically efficient, the contact center requires an appropriate level of technology. "Appropriate" is a slippery word. Chapter 3 portrayed a road map of sorts through contact center technologies. As the mission and scope of the contact center expands, operational excellence depends upon quality tools.

The second meaning has to do with a common error found in many contact centers: *inadequate management staff.* It is not uncommon to find the supervisor-to-agent ratio in excess of 1:20. In some cases supervisors attempt to manage as many as 50 agents. It cannot be done. Study after study has found that a useful management span of control is about 10 to 15 people.

A related problem exists where the ratio between supervisors and agents is more favorable but the supervisors are called "lead agents" and are expected to handle calls, as well as provide supervision to the agents in their group. Why is the ratio between supervisors and agents is so important? Because their primary task is to coach struggling agents. Effective coaching takes time.

Other areas where contact centers usually fail themselves is in the areas of *technical support, training and clerical staff.* As the systems become more complex and as multiple subsystems are tightly integrated, like voice mail and interactive voice response, it is absolutely necessary to create a technical support position. This person will be the focus for all vendor-provided training and will become the technical expert that the contact center relies upon.

Training should be an ongoing activity—something that you never finish even if your center is not growing. It makes great sense for the center to have its own training support. The training effort encompasses policy and procedure, navigation of computer screens, telephone etiquette, call control, stress management, product knowledge and other subjects. Not only will courses have to be acquired or developed in these areas but the management process unfolding here will also require specialized, highly targeted remedial training sessions.

There is a lot of resistance to clerical staff in business today because of emphasis on expense reduction and a growing expectation that employees are capable of being entirely self-reliant. This is particularly ironic in a contact center environment. One of the biggest problems facing contact center managers has to do with keeping agents on the telephones. There are usually many legitimate reasons that can pull agents away from the phones. Faxes, copying, interoffice correspondence, tracking down specific information, pulling centralized paper files and related tasks are more properly the province of clerical workers. An experienced, tenured agent should be recognized as a highly skilled employee whose value is too high to waste on no-skill-required tasks. In the preceding chapter the Erlang tables were used to dramatically reveal what happens to service levels when just a few agents leave their positions. The statistical charts met the real world recently. The management team for a medical technology company was puzzled over the poor service level in their order entry application because they felt they were staffed adequately. After analyzing the average sign-on time and make-busy time, it was concluded that there were far too many tasks that took the agents away from their positions. The center added a couple of clerks (at far less than agent wages) and the service level improved dramatically.

The Two Basic Balances

One of the myths mentioned earlier had to do with what many consider a natural conflict between productivity and quality. Conventional wisdom says that you can't have both. Let it be emphasized that in order to have a truly world-class contact center you must have both! The way to achieve this duality has to do with maintaining two balances.

The first balance is to focus and work to improve both productivity and quality simultaneously. Contact centers that stress just one component for a time tend to experience the myth in a very direct way. It is as if productivity and quality were linked according to the following diagram:

Figure 6-3. Balancing Productivity and Quality

Thinking about productivity and quality as if they were weights on a balance beam is the exact right way to avoid whipsawing agents. The contact center manager must always equally stress quality with productivity. Sometimes it is not evident why this must be the case. The usual error is to stress productivity over quality. After all, calls must be answered. If productivity is not high enough, the calls will not be answered within the service level goal.

But consider the effects that poor quality generates. The many effects of poor quality within the contact center itself and in the company include:
- Escalation of calls to upper management
- Repeat calls from customers
- Callbacks to customers for missing or incomplete information
- Cancellations
- Costs associated with closing accounts
- Costs associated with product returns
- Unnecessary service calls
- Wrong problems get fixed
- Calls to customer relations
- Diversion of agents to unnecessary tasks
- Incremental shipping expenses to reship correct item
- Loss of referrals
- Incremental talk time

It is ironic that many of the outcomes associated with poor quality in the contact center impact the contact center in a very direct way. Sometimes it is a shock for the contact center manager to realize that poor quality is the cause of rising call volumes and lengthened talk times. In the face of these two dynamics, service levels deteriorate faster. Management could react by demanding higher productivity, which might result in even poorer quality. A vicious circle is created. The bottom-line message is that you *need to work on both quality and productivity equally* in order to succeed in the contact center.

If you make the commitment to working on quality and productivity equally, the second basic balance comes into play.

Productivity   **CSR Morale**
& Quality   **& Growth**

Figure 6-4. P&Q Balance with CSR Morale & Growth

The only way to get long-lasting improvements in productivity and quality is to recognize that the agents need to be supported and given an opportunity to grow in the skills required by their jobs.

Manage at the Individual Agent Level

You might think that this would be self-evident but it is not. The problem is that the service level actually provided is a group function. No single agent is responsible for the service level. It becomes seductively simple to begin to think in group terms. The group gets rewarded when the service level goal is exceeded. The group gets a motivational speech when the goal is unmet.

This group orientation has serious negative consequences.

Whether the group is meeting the service level goal or not, this management style sends inappropriate messages to certain subgroups within the larger group.

In a contact center agent group it is not unusual to find a distribution of agent performance something like the graph below. You might recognize this as a normal distribution curve. It is a typical representation of performance in any large human population.

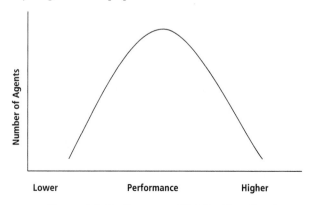

Figure 6-5. Performance Distribution Graph

If the service level goal unmet and the agents are exhorted to do better, there is a high risk of demotivating the hard-working agents. After all, they might naturally think, how much more can we be expected to give? Similarly, if the group is meeting the goal and management praises their efforts, what incentive does the underachieving agent have to improve?

Performance Visible to Individual Agents

As mentioned earlier, a contact center is an invisible world and the dynamics that occur routinely in other environments just don't happen in there. It is in the realm of performance where this is most evident.

In a visible work environment, employees can see how their peers perform their functions. An employee can observe different approaches to common situations. Workers learn from each other. Another aspect is that workers develop a sense of performance expectations. This happens even when management fails to explicitly inform workers about performance standards.

This doesn't happen in a contact center. Telephone calls are relatively private interactions. An agent rarely hears how a peer deals with a caller. The same can be said for handling e-mail messages. Vocabularies are very different among a group of people. Because people are more sophisticated these days, agents are aware that performance measurements are being taken when they go to work in a contact center. Agents know that the contact center management has access to performance figures.

While consulting, contact center agents were frequently asked two questions:
1. Do you know what the performance standard is here?
2. Do you know what your actual performance is?

Most of the time the answers to both questions are the same—no! Agents deserve to have clear standards of performance spelled out in writing. They also have a right to know how they are actually performing against that standard of performance. If you fail to do this, agents will engage in behaviors that reduce the stress imposed by the undefined situation. First, they will fret and worry about performance. After some time, they will cease to worry about performance. After more time, they will become cold and callused regarding performance. This attitude, unfortunately, can be transmitted during a transaction.

Center Managed in Real Time and 15- or 30-Minute Intervals

Although this sounds suspiciously nonsensical, it is absolutely necessary for contact center management to observe both timelines in order to become a world-class contact center. Put simply, you must pre-plan for each interval of the day and then react to deviations from your plan as required by the moment.

You can know that each day calls will be received in some arrival pattern. Call volume varies by day of week, day of month and month of year. In some applications, other variables play a role in changing call volume. Not only do call volumes vary, but talk time varies as well. The call volume and the talk time constitute the offered workload. It is a requirement for all contact centers to have some mechanism, process or software tool that forecasts call volume and talk time. Ideally, such a process or tool will use sophisticated algorithms that use the actual historical data from the contact center as input to the forecast. Armed with a reasonable forecast, management can ensure that the correct number of agents are in place for each time period of the day. This is called "getting in the ballpark." Contact center managers must "get in the ballpark" with forecasting and staff scheduling if they have any intention of reaching and maintaining differentiated, high-quality services. But getting in the ballpark is only part of the solution.

The reality is that the best forecast will be 90 to 95% accurate. Do you remember from the Erlang case study what happens to service levels when just 10% of the agents leave their positions? It was stated then that if any variable changed by just 10%, the impact upon service level was identical to some agents leaving their positions. Since our forecast has a very good chance of being wrong by as much as 5 to 10%, you must also manage in real time. If you are lucky, you have a system that permits you to establish transaction routing rules with self-monitoring performance capabilities. Recall the discussion on conditional routing. If you are not lucky, you need to have someone keeping an eye on the service levels of each important application in the contact center. They will also need a written action plan to guide them in taking appropriate action.

The Primary Role of Supervisors

This is no longer as controversial as it once was. At more and more contact centers, everyone seems to agree that the most important thing supervisors can do with their time is to work with struggling agents to help them become proficient. What is interesting here is the fact that many supervisors have been promoted from agent ranks where they demonstrated skills in handling transactions. Outside of escalation, supervisors don't usually handle transactions. They handle agents.
This is a much different skill-set. Or is it?

If asked to judge whether a particular person is a good supervisor or a poor supervisor, how would you decide? How are supervisors judged? What are they responsible for? A single supervisor can't be responsible for the group service level except when the entire agent group fits into the supervisor span of control. So, many supervisors cannot be evaluated on service level. How can we evaluate them? This is not meant to denigrate the role of supervisor. They are critical to a contact center but their talents and energies are wasted when all they do is to take attendance, prepare paper reports, enforce break and lunch times and run around when the queue starts to grow. On the other hand, it is easy to judge supervisors based on how well they develop their subordinates and manage time. You can avoid subjectivity because staff development can be inferred through performance measurements over time. So, supervisors who were great agents might have an advantage when coaching is emphasized.

A Contact Center Management Philosophy

There are only three resources a manager can employ to achieve success in the contact center: technology, the agents and management skill.

While the technology is fascinating, it is merely a tool. Relationship-building interactions happen only when a caller is connected to an agent or a well-designed self-help resource, like voice recognition IVRs or interactive Web sites. Agents are the primary resource in the contact center.

A fundamental belief is that people are not lazy; they need to work because of economic necessity. People also work because they want to achieve and feel good about themselves. Everyone finds satisfaction in doing something well. We seem to be "wired" this way. Achieving mastery in some skill provides for a sense of accomplishment and satisfaction.

From this, it is a logical extension to identify certain basic rights that workers should possess. Workers have a right to know exactly what is expected of them. Therefore, the workplace should have clear goals and standards of performance. Workers have a right to know how they are performing. Not just annually during a mandatory salary review, but continuously. If workers receive unbiased, objective feedback on a regular basis, most of the trauma and emotion of the annual review will disappear. Finally, workers have a right to be improved in their ability to do their jobs. This last statement usually raises some eyebrows. It shouldn't. If a business presumes to measure workers in terms of performance, it seems appropriate to suppose that the business knows the skills and knowledge inventory that is necessary to master the job. Once the business judges a particular employee as deficient in one or more areas, it seems fair for the employee to turn to the business and ask to be improved in his/her abilities.

Transforming Principles into a Process

Translating problems, issues, dynamics, observations and principles into a management process moves us from generalities to specifics. Be aware of the difference between a strategy and a tactic. In order to profit from the stock market you must buy low and sell high. That is a strategy. The tactics that embody this strategy are what separates stock market winners from losers. While we admit that there are multiple ways to implement our contact center management philosophy (the strategy), please consider using the process and approach described in the next section (the tactics).

Contact Centers—A Management Process

A word of warning is in order. What is about to be proposed in the following pages might be perceived negatively by people in the contact center. Change, no matter small or large, is frequently resisted by the people it affects. Sociologists believe that the reason people resist change has to do with fear of the unknown. For this reason, it is imperative that you establish a *people-centered environment*. A people-centered contact center environment exists when:

- The entire resources of the contact center are focused upon making the agents successful.
- Agent performance goals are well-defined and complimentary to the goals set for the entire contact center.
- Regular supervisor/agent team meetings are scheduled and held.
- Communication flows freely in both directions; from management to the agents and agents to management.
- Recognition and reward exists for excellent agent performance.

It should be pointed out that establishing this environment is not easy. Some contact centers suffer from a basic conflict between the agents and center management. The essence of the conflict has to do with power and authority. Agents understand that center management has the power and authority to strip them of their livelihoods. Management understands that their career success is dependent upon the actions and behaviors of the agents. The conflict arises when distrust enters the equation from either side. Dark-side management practices, defined as management by threat, can take root. Agents respond to the implied job-loss threat by indulging in passive aggression and/or "satisficing" performance, defined as doing the minimum acceptable.

Facilitating Change

There are two ways that the contact center manager can choose to implement the changes suggested here. First, the manager can impose the changes by dictate. Simply announce that these things are going to be done. This approach looks like the quickest way to incorporate change but the efficiency is illusory. People tend to resist change because they believe that the proposed change will mean, in some way, that their work-lives will be harder, less satisfying or more restricted than before. People display very negative reactions to innocuous change imposed by dictate.

A second way change can be implemented is by hiring a third party, such as a consultant, or playing the role of consultant yourself. The better consultants use education to help sell the change to the affected employees. In addition, the consultant is properly viewed as having no "agenda" in the matter being discussed. This is a great way to jump-start change in your contact center. Consultants frequently use the principle of guided discovery, which involves education of a selected group as to the nature of the problems and possible solutions. The group is asked to consider all the solutions and either choose a solution, modify one or create an entirely new solution. The group also helps sell the changes to the rest of the employees, which they can do because they helped create the change.

To minimize resistance to change, you may want to create a re-engineering team. The size of this team depends upon the size of the contact center. In a center of about 50 agents, a re-engineering team of 6 to 10 people would be appropriate. The team should include the contact center manager, several supervisors, a majority of agents, a member of quality assurance (if this function exists) and a member of training (if this function exists). The agents selected for the re-engineering team should be a good cross-section of the center population. Don't just select high-performers, experienced agents or strong team players. Include a few relatively new agents. Select at least one agent who has some tenure but has never achieved high performance. Try to select people who display a willingness to speak their opinions.

The role of the re-engineering team is nothing less than the reinvention of the entire contact center. This team is not meant to be a rubber stamp for the desires and agenda of the contact center manager. The manager is primarily a resource to the re-engineering team, but can and does act to define acceptable limits. The best results can be obtained if the manager guides team discussions at appropriate times. This is a tricky role to execute. Too little guidance and the re-engineering team might formulate ideas and plans at odds with the best interests of the contact center and company. Too much guidance and it will come to see itself as a mere rubber stamp. This is why this role is so well played by a consultant. In fact, the manager or consultant will guide the team towards certain preconceived ideas, plans and programs, like the ones identified in this book. This might appear cynical. It is not. The results of a re-engineering team approach are far superior to simply stating that the center is going to adopt new policies and procedures.

A useful starting point for the re-engineering team is a statement of fact by the contact center manager to the effect that the center is working too hard and not achieving enough. Facts regarding performance should be presented to the group. Among the more powerful facts that should be shared will be the service level attainment for the center over the past several months. The manager should attempt to explain to the team why the contact center is important to the goals of the company. The manager should inform the team that *they* are going to work to create a new contact center environment that will produce improved performance.

Certain elements of the environment will require discussion. Those elements are:
- MIS Reports
- Skill and Knowledge Inventory
- Recognition and Support

One final rule needs to be understood by all team members. Everything discussed in the team meetings is to be shared with all the agents without reservation. The reason for this is to break the rumor channels that invariably exist in every human organization. When a re-engineering team is established, word will quickly spread throughout the contact center about the members and the purpose. The agents must understand what is going on inside the team. It is important that they have some casual access to the thought processes and ideas that lead to recommendations. Casual interaction between members of the re-engineering team and the rest of the agent population are *key* to the acceptance of the changes that will result. It is also a useful way for members of the re-engineering team to bring ideas, concerns and opinions to the team from the agent population. All this is fundamental to change "buy-in."

MIS Reports

Mentioned earlier was the fact that it is difficult to extract real value from most system reports. The standard reports are usually columns and rows of numbers. The time perspective is either a single day or a summarized time period like a week or a month. Even the newer graphical representations of this data lack crispness, precision and clarity. A suggestion is the creation of a small set of highly graphic reports that will be shared with the entire contact center population. These reports are designed to achieve two things: (1) to break down the invisible world of the contact center, and (2) to identify processes and people in need of improvement and coaching.

The first report format you might consider is the "Worst Half-Hour Report." This is primarily a high-level diagnostic tool, although some centers share it with the agent population, as well. The report format is presented here in figure 6-6:

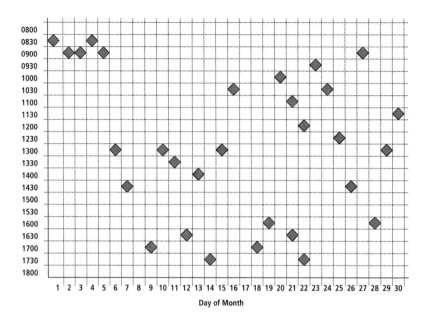

Figure 6-6. Worst Half-Hour Service Level Chart

Along the x-axis is a time line in days. The y-axis is scaled with clock time coinciding with the center's hours of operation. A point represents the particular half-hour of the day when the contact center experiences its worst half-hour in terms of service level attainment or ASA. Use one color for voice calls. Use a second color for e-mail transaction processing where the most messages violated the service level agreement your company made to the senders. You might also consider using a third color for the time of day when the most Web site service help requests went unfulfilled. Over time a pattern should emerge. Sometimes you will find a series of points at the same time of day over many days. This indicates that there is something structurally wrong with staffing during that half-hour. Many times this chart reveals that breaks or lunches are being handled incorrectly, considering the workload.

W. Edwards Deming, considered the guru of productivity and quality processes, would be pleased with this approach. After identifying a particular half-hour as a consistent problem, the obvious response is to attempt to fix it. If successful, another worst half-hour will emerge at some other time of day. The Deming philosophy, in part, states that the quest for higher productivity and quality is endless. There will *always* be a worst half-hour no matter what you do. The goal, in terms of this chart, is to remedy all structural and operational causes so that the center's worst half-hour is somewhat random.

Another basic chart to consider is the "Average Sign-On Time Report." One of the most basic problems affecting contact centers is agent time erosion, listed as one of the problems that plague all contact centers. It is difficult to keep agents at their stations or on the phones. There are lots of legitimate things that take agents away from their work. In addition to scheduled breaks and lunches, agents will take unscheduled "casual breaks." When an agent "has to go," they will go. There are many other things that take agents away from the phones like retrieving files, asking questions of supervisors and using office equipment.

It is unpleasant for supervisors to be forced into becoming time police. No supervisor likes watching the clock, keeping time, searching restrooms and nagging agents to get back to their desks. With this report, there won't be as much need to do that.

First, ask the agents among the re-engineering team if they are aware of the rules surrounding agent work-states. Usually, ACD vendors provide for several agent work-states. They are:

Available	Talking on Incoming Call
Unavailable	Idle
Wrap-Up	Talking on Outbound Call
Conference Call	Talking on Internal Call

It has been found that many times there is no written policy in the contact center regarding the use of these work-states. This is a serious problem because it invalidates the data being collected by the system. For example, if one agent uses the idle work-state for breaks while another signs off the system, there is no way to compare the two agents in terms of sign-on time or useful productivity measures! The following work-state rules produce some good outcomes in later reports:

Sign-On: Promptly at the beginning of scheduled shifts, ready to work.

Sign-Off: Lunch, scheduled breaks, meetings, special projects and end of shift. If the technology allows, there should be a sign-off reason so that the time can be accounted for.

Wrap-Up: Work or other activities directly related to the *preceding* transaction. Includes short questions to your supervisor, online entries and related paperwork.

Idle or Unavailable: Casual breaks, extended talks with supervisor, getting a beverage to bring back to station (if permitted).

Second, have the re-engineering team perform an exercise. (Keep track of the discussion with entries on a white board.) For each kind of work tour, start with the number of hours. A full-time agent might normally work eight hours a day. Subtract break and lunch time. Discuss other legitimate routine activities that take an agent away from the phones. You might end up with a white board that looks like the following example:

Scheduled Hours		8.00
1st Break	.25	
Lunch	.5	
2nd Break	.25	
Casual Breaks	.25	
Meetings	.25	
Subtotal	1.50	
Expected Sign-On Hours		6.50

Deming, mentioned previously, suggests that instead of a discrete goal (like exactly 6.5 sign-on hours), it is more useful, less heavy-handed and more reflective of reality to create a "band" of acceptable performance for any measurement criteria. Additionally, it is mandatory that measurements like this be taken as an average of at least five days. Ten working days are preferred. So, expect to create and publish an Average Sign-On chart every two weeks. A useful format example follows:

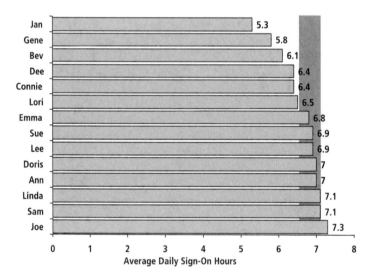

Figure 6-7. Average Sign-On Chart

The chart shows average sign-on time for a full-time agent group. A Deming band of acceptable performance is included. Notice that agent names are displayed. This can be a source of some spirited discussion among the members of the re-engineering team because, in many instances, agents feel that publication of personal data is akin to an invasion of privacy or potentially embarrassing. Some centers will decide to substitute numerical IDs in place of agent names. Some centers decide to publish the chart with no identification but inform each agent privately which bar belongs to them. It probably really doesn't matter. If you are successful in creating a people-centered environment, agents will not feel threatened by having their names on the charts. If there are problems with displaying names, settle for IDs. After a few iterations of the chart, agents will begin to learn the IDs of their friends and soon it won't matter anymore.

If there is an agent time-shrinkage problem in your contact center, this chart will reveal it. If you obtain re-engineering team approval to post this report on bulletin boards around the contact center, the problem will largely disappear from the center overnight. It's not that agents are stealing time in a hurtful manner. Usually it's more a matter of misunderstood policy. Perhaps a few agents get a little sloppy with time management. Most often, by the second report cycle just about all agents have bars in the Deming band. You can ease any negative perceptions by permitting agents to have supervisors add time when justified to the report data. Meanwhile, agents should remind supervisors that they were assigned to an off-phone project and to please add or make adjustment to the Average Sign-On report. With this and other agent-related reports, explain to the re-engineering team why the data is important (the hypothetical contact center example is a good place for ideas on this), how it is collected and *re-emphasize* that it is not a report card. All the reports are diagnostic tools designed to identify problems so that solutions can be found. Nobody should feel threatened.

Measuring Productivity

The more important MIS reports have to do with measuring productivity and quality. A very wise person once claimed that if you can't measure something, you cannot truly manage it. The definition of productivity in your contact center should make for an interesting discussion among the re-engineering team members. Useful measures depend upon the applications in your contact center.

In revenue centers a typical productivity measure might be dollars per hour. Contact center managers ought to use caution about keying on dollars. The caution comes about because the agents receive callers in a random way. Callers may or may not be ready to buy and, in any case, the amount they buy is not always influenced by the skills of the agent. If dollars per hour is deemed a good measure by the re-engineering team, insist that this measure be taken over a lengthy time period. Avoid this statistic when it represents a single day's data.

While there might be many ways to get at productivity depending upon the application, one universal productivity measurement for voice calls exists: calls per hour. We will cover multimedia productivity and quality measurements a little later. Reports from the major contact center vendors provide a lot of data on agent performance, but it still takes time and work on the part of the manager to dig the information out. There are many problems associated with the data presented by the standard reports. Agents work different hours. Agents work in different shifts. These complications, among others, make it difficult—if not impossible—to directly compare agent productivity from the standard reports.

Statistics provides a simple formula that normalizes agent productivity data on an hourly basis. This formula compensates for different call arrival rates, different shifts and different work hours. It permits all agents who handle the same kind of transaction to be directly compared with each other. It is referred to as Normalized Calls per Hour. The formula is:

$$\text{Normalized Calls per Hour} = \frac{\text{Number of Calls Handled}}{\text{(Sign-On Time) - (Available Time)}}$$

Take the number of calls handled by a particular agent and divide by total sign-on time minus the total time the agent spends waiting for the next call. Most ACD systems refer to this time as available time. Some use the term wait time. All systems capture this data but sometimes you have to work backwards from other data elements. This formula works well. It rewards two very good kinds of agent behavior; taking calls and being ready to take calls.

The first application of this formula is to produce a Normalized Calls per Hour chart for the entire contact center. If you have multiple, independent queues and specialized agent groups, you might consider producing a chart for each instead of one for the entire contact center. A typical format for this chart follows:

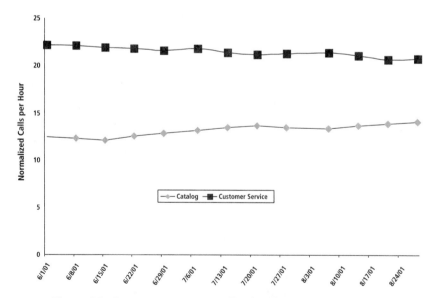

Figure 6-8. Contact center Normalized Calls per Hour by Queue

Along the x-axis place the time line in days. The y-axis is a scale for normalized calls per hour for either the center or each functional group. The calculation is fairly simple. Divide the total calls handled by the total agent sign-on time minus the total agent available time. Since day-to-day movements don't mean much, consider using a two-week reporting cycle. Every two weeks calculate the normalized center productivity figure. This is a very useful chart to post in the contact center for all agents to observe.

A more obvious use of the normalizing formula is to produce a Normalized Calls per Hour chart by agent. A typical format for this chart appears below:

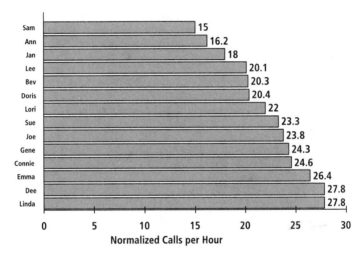

Figure 6-9. Normalized Calls Per Hour by Agent

This chart should look like the Average Sign-On chart discussed earlier. The data should reflect the same time period. If you have decided to do a 2-week reporting cycle, use it consistently with all reports that apply to agent measurements to smooth the random nature of call arrivals and transaction types. Special note for contact centers that have embraced skill routing: You should produce a separate chart for each skill defined in the center. For example, if an agent can handle sales calls and customer service calls, you should produce a chart that shows performance in each separate function. This can get tricky, but the re-engineering team can agree to whatever seems to work for them. Again, the same cautions apply as were discussed in relation to the Average Sign-On report. Be diplomatic. Remember that one of the earlier "contact center realities" stated that the productivity differential between experienced, tenured agents was quite large. In some cases it can be a three-to-one difference. This is normal. It begins to reveal the productivity improvement potential that exists in every contact center.

When the first normalized calls per hour chart is produced for review by the re-engineering team, prepare for some surprise among the members.

Most contact centers do not provide agents with performance data. Therefore, most agents judge themselves to perform "about average." When the report is passed around the room there will be some silence as the information is absorbed. Then there is usually a steady stream of comments. Soon there are questions about why the data looks this way.

To begin to answer that question, a very useful report is Average Transaction Time by Agent. A typical example is provided below:

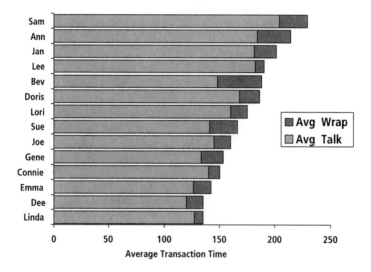

Figure 6-10. Average Transaction Time by Agent

This is a stacked bar chart identifying the two components of agent transaction time; talk time (spent with the caller) and wrap-up time. Wrap-up time is sometimes called "after-call work" and refers to appropriate and necessary work related to the call just completed. Not all contact center applications require wrap-up time since the advent of online data retrieval. Of course, there is a direct correlation between transaction time and normalized productivity. What is surprising is the extreme variability in talk times and wrap-up times among the agent population.

The re-engineering team should be educated that the differences in transaction times and its components do not reflect attitude so much as it reflects the fact that initial training for the complex job of agent usually does not equip the average person to master the job. Remind yourself and the team about the fact that there is no such thing as on-the-job training in a contact center.

There are some interesting outcomes associated with publishing this set of productivity reports. Usually, the productivity superstar is surprised at his/her ranking. Trainees and new-hires appear at the low end of the productivity range but a few tenured agents will appear there, as well.

There is a renewed interest from the agent population in understanding how the calculations are made. Great care should be taken to fully explain the process and how the calculations work. The Transaction Time report is a marvelous tool. It can be used to show agents, at least at a high level, why their productivity is what it is. It is particularly compelling to show an agent with excellent average talk time that the reason their productivity is lower than it might otherwise be is because their average wrap-up time is excessive. Or it might be the other way around; long average talk time with short wrap-up. The best outcome that can be imagined is that agents who are friends will begin to have some focused conversations regarding how they accomplish their jobs. This begins to pierce the veil in the invisible world of contact centers.

Multiskilled Agent Productivity Measures

As more contact centers turn towards skill routing solutions, measuring productivity becomes more difficult. I guess that this is just another instance of the fact that there is no such thing as a free lunch. An example serves to illustrate the potential problem.

Suppose we have three agents who are skilled in three very different kinds of transactions. We'll call these transactions Types A, B and C. Further, because these transactions are different from each other, they also have different average handle times. Let us suppose that the average transaction time for Type A is 180 seconds, for Type B is 60 seconds and for Type C is 360 seconds.

Now suppose that we have three agents, named Agent X, Agent Y and Agent Z, respectively. Here is the important assumption for our illustration: Each agent performs at exactly the average transaction time. Because they are multiskilled they can receive any of the three call types. For illustration purposes we capture a short segment of time and find that the agents have handled the following calls:

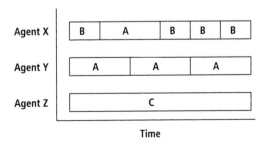

Figure 6-11. Multiskilled Agent Illustration

What the chart shows is that Agent X has handled 5 transactions, Agent Y has handled 3 transactions and Agent Z has handled 1 transaction. If we use the Normalized Calls per Hour formula (described earlier in this chapter) to quantify their productivity, we get nonsense answers. That is because the transactions have very different handle times. We can take extra effort and produce a NCPH chart by transaction type for each agent. The only problem we have is how to portion Available time between the transaction types.

What might be useful is some kind of higher level chart that management could use to determine whether a more in-depth analysis is even warranted. There is a clear need for such a tool. As multiskilling becomes more prevalent and the number of skills we define expands, this problem will become more pernicious. This is why systems that provide a single-line summary of an agent's performance are undesirable. They disguise too much and reveal too little.

There will be many furrowed brows before a good solution is found for this problem. I suspect that some higher level metric might be useful to, at minimum, help contact center managers understand whether they need to do a deeper analysis. I propose that consideration be given to what I call a Work Unit Index. The Work Unit Index formula is as follows:

Work Unit Index = N(TA − TAa) + N(TB − TBa) + N(TC − TCa)

If we use this formula with our hypothetical agents we would have the following:

Agent X Work Unit Index = 1 (180 − 180) + 4 (60 − 60) = 0

If we do this for each of the agents in our example, we would find that their Work Unit Index figures are all zero. That is because we made an assumption that they worked each transaction at exactly the center average handle time. The value zero indicates that we don't have to examine these agents in any greater depth.

Note that the formula produces a positive number when the agent is performing better than the center averages for each transaction and produces a negative number when the agent is performing below the center averages. Also note that when an agent is handling multiple, different-length transactions and is better in some than in others, the formula will produce higher negative numbers when an agent is getting a lot of transactions that he/she is handling worse than the center average handle time. This serves as a flag to management that perhaps a deeper analysis should be undertaken on that agent and that he/she might be considered for supplemental training in that transaction type.

Measuring Quality

Remember the two basic balances? Before you publish a productivity report, you must implement a way to measure quality—never do one without the other. There are several approaches to measuring quality in a contact center. Consider the following:

1. You can judge quality by adopting the caller's perspective. Assume quality is provided if the caller is satisfied with the outcome of the transaction or interaction.
2. You can measure quality by surveying the callers either through the mail, transferring them to "quality control" agents or by calling them back. Asking a series of questions and soliciting responses permits a quality measurement to be produced.
3. You can attempt to automate the above process by transferring callers to an IVR system that asks questions and records responses.

There are problems associated with all these approaches. The main problem with point one has to do with caller satisfaction. While it may be desirable to suppose that high quality always means the customer is right and gets their way, it is unrealistic. The customer is not always right. Take, for example, a caller to a bank customer service organization who has just been notified of an overdraft situation. In many financial organizations an overdraft on an account means that a fee will be charged to the account holder. If it is bank policy that this fee will not be waived, the caller will probably not be satisfied at the outcome of their call. If we were to talk to this customer immediately after the conversation with the bank agent, there is a high probability that the customer would portray the telephone interaction as poor *no matter how the agent behaved*. Clearly, judging quality by the caller's perception carries the risk that something else will be judged.

Similar problems exist for the points two and three. If you contact callers after the transaction in an attempt to survey them for quality considerations, the same problem will surely be encountered—the caller's perspective is heavily influenced by the outcome and not by the process of the call itself. In the case of a call-back, add the problem of expense.

In an effort to reduce costs, a few companies have tried the approach in point three. Using an IVR, it is felt, has several advantages. Because a human is not involved, conventional wisdom has it that callers will be more likely to reveal their true emotions about the contact center interaction. Callers can be transferred to the IVR immediately after the transaction while the experience is fresh in their minds. There are problems associated with this approach, as well. The biggest problem is that there is a high likelihood that only callers whose emotions are at either end of the scale will agree to complete the IVR survey. In other words, if the caller is very angry or very pleased they are likely to interact with the IVR quality survey script. The nearer to neutral a caller's attitude is, the more likely they will hang up after completing the agent interaction. Moreover, it seems that everyone is in too big a rush to take a few extra minutes for anything.

Having identified some problems with these approaches, please be assured that all these approaches to measuring quality need to be undertaken. They are important glimpses into the psyche of your customer population. However, we need to measure quality at an individual agent level. The solution that works best joins silent monitoring and single-pass scoring with rigorous quality criteria. And the criteria should focus upon company and contact center policy, product/service knowledge and call handling skills. Silent monitoring itself is a semi-controversial issue in contact centers. But, the quality of customer handling cannot be measured, managed or even improved without silent monitoring.

Most states in the United States permit silent monitoring as long as one party to the conversation is aware of the practice. Worldwide, similar guidelines are in place. I am told that strong German unions have made it very difficult to perform any monitoring of conversations, which is a most perplexing problem. For protection, have agents sign an agreement indicating that they are aware that silent monitoring is used to manage quality. Make it a condition of employment with new hires. Assure all the agents that monitoring will be random and evenly applied. Indicate that the telephones in the break area are to be used for personal calls and will never be subject to monitoring. In states with more rigorous laws, it may be necessary to force all callers to hear an announcement informing them that calls may be monitored for quality. A few states require an audible tone to be periodically generated during monitored conversations. Whatever actions you have to take to comply with local laws are worth the effort.

Before any monitoring takes place, take subjectivity out of the process. There is a way to do this. Record on cassette tape actual conversations from the contact center. You will need about 20 taped conversations per session. Assemble the personnel that will be performing quality monitoring. Some large organizations have a separate quality assurance group, while most contact centers use supervisors in this role. A few contact centers use both supervisors and agents in a peer-review fashion. If agreement can be obtained from the re-engineering team to move forward with peer review quality monitoring, you will experience the greatest potential for improvement.

With the quality monitoring team assembled, start a discussion on the topic of what, exactly, constitutes quality in the contact center. The conversation will quickly devolve into generalities, but it is worth the time. This sets up the group for the real exercise. Portray the exercise as a game. The rules of the game are simple. A previously recorded call will be played to the group. There should be no talking, no gestures, no groans, no smiles and no interactions among the group while the recorded call is being played. After the recorded call finishes playing, immediately have every member of the group judge the quality of that call using a form like the one here in figure 6-12:

```
                    QUALITY SCORE SHEET

    Call  | Excellent  |  Good  | Fair |  Poor
     1
     2
     3
     4
     5
     6
     7
     8
     9
    10
    Totals
    Weight:     Excellent ___ x 1.0 = ___
                Good      ___ x 2/3 = ___
                Fair      ___ x 1/3 = ___
                Poor      ___ x  0  = ___
```

Figure 6-12. Typical Quality Score Sheet

The idea is to label the call as being Excellent, Good, Fair or Poor with respect to quality after listening to the call just once. Sometimes it is useful to provide a guideline regarding the differences between the four rankings. The following generalized definitions have been adopted in other contact centers and work well:

Excellent—Nothing noted that could improve the call.

Good—Satisfactory call in knowledge and application of skills. Minor improvements could be made.

Fair—Shows a basic understanding of job knowledge and customer handling skills, yet certain areas require improvement.

Poor—Information given is incorrect and/or customer handling is poor. Serious deficiency in one or more areas (e.g., lack of job understanding, divisional policies, job requirements, job knowledge or skills, application of knowledge or skills, etc.)

Once the quality monitors have judged the recorded call, go around the room and ask each monitor how they ranked the call. You will see a good deal of variability in the rankings. Quality is subjective. Then ask several monitors why they ranked the recorded call as they did. The reasons given will be all over the place. This forms the basis for free and open discussions among the quality monitors. You may be horrified at some of the reasons offered. You will discover that the quality monitors have very different perceptions of policy, procedure and even product/service knowledge. This is normal and represents just another aspect of the insidious invisible world of contact centers.

As this quality monitoring exercise progresses, you will discover that certain policies are poorly understood or not understood at all. There will be gaps in policy and procedure. Desirable behaviors have not been identified in writing or have not been consistently communicated to the agent population. All these things are good. You are flushing out some of the structural impediments to both productivity and quality in your contact center! With each reviewed call, the quality team will uncover more and more gaps, holes and misunderstandings. And, they will begin to converge in their scoring. It might take from three to five sessions like this to achieve scoring consistency. A note on this: Perfectly consistent scoring need not be achieved. What will be implemented is a quality measurement process with some checks and safeguards that help to ensure even bias across the agent population and among quality monitors.

When the quality monitors are providing fairly convergent scoring, it is time to execute. Each agent should be quality-scored on at least ten calls over the same time frame as productivity reporting. More samples are always better. Again, ten working days or two calendar weeks is a useful time perspective. Obviously, the total agent population will need to be quality-scored. Each quality monitor will have some calculable number of monitoring sessions to perform.

To help avoid unintentional bias, a particular agent should be quality-scored by at least two or three different quality monitors. There are some operational issues to be worked out here. An inelegant but workable solution consists of creating a quality score sheet for each agent. Each agent's supervisor will do some number of quality monitors and pass the individual agent folders to another quality monitor. Who to pass folders to is largely a matter of agreement among those involved. The pattern should recognize natural groupings among the agent population. For example, there may be 45 agents in customer service. Perhaps there are three supervisors with each having responsibility for 15 agents. Each supervisor performs four quality-monitoring sessions with their own agents and three sessions with each agent in the two other teams. It is probably not a good idea to mix quality monitors across applications. Properly trained monitors can hear and judge quality in a single pass when they have experience with the nature of the transaction.

The weighting given to the four quality categories is entirely up to the contact center manager. There are some interesting results when the perfect quality score is quantified as at or above the highest practical productivity score. There are 3,600 seconds in an hour. If your average talk time is 120 seconds, then the highest practical calls-per-hour score will be 30. Can't do better. If the highest calls-per-hour score is 30, then the highest quality score should be 30. This can be set by making the value of the Excellent category equal to three.

Putting Productivity and Quality Scoring Together

It's time to bring it all together. You have normalized calls per hour as a productivity measure. Now you have quality scores. Both are produced during the same time span. All this work produces a very simple, deceptively powerful chart. The following format works well:

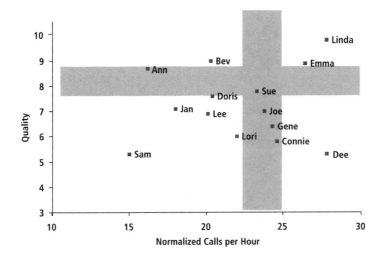

Figure 6-13. Quality/Productivity Chart

This chart weaves several threads together. Along the vertical axis is the quality score scale. This example uses the scoring values indicated on the Quality Score Sheet figure earlier, where the maximum quality score is ten. Along the horizontal axis is the productivity scale. A point represents both values. In our example, Emma has a productivity score of 26 and a quality score of 8.5. Similarly, Sam has a productivity score of 15 and a quality score of 5.3. The re-engineering team has determined the Deming bands for each measurement.

On a single page, it's easy to array the Quality/Productivity (Q/P) points for a supervisor group or even the entire agent group. At a glance the chart reveals four classes of agents. In the upper right-hand quadrant are the superstar agents. These agents deliver consistent high productivity *and* high quality. In the lower right-hand quadrant are agents that have mastered productivity issues but are having some problem with quality components. In the upper left-hand quadrant are the agents who consistently deliver high quality but appear to have some productivity problems. And, in the lower left-hand quadrant are agents who appear to be struggling, like Sam.

Apart from this neat compartmentalizing of the agent force, what is the point of this chart? It must be emphasized that it is not a report card. It is not meant to embarrass or intimidate anyone. It is a tool through which supervisors can attempt to fulfill their primary role—to help struggling agents become proficient. Since supervisors never have enough time in their schedules to accomplish everything that needs doing, it is mandatory that some tool exist to help identify agents who are in the most need of the scarce help resources. This is the entire point of the chart. Later, this chapter discusses how this chart makes contests and recognition programs absolutely fair and understandable.

The Q/P chart should observe the same conventions as established for the other agent reports. If names are permitted, display them. Otherwise use IDs. If no identity is the preferred mode, you will have to provide individual copies of the reports with the individual agent's data elements identified privately. However, some public display of the reports and charts are necessary to further break down the invisible environment of contact centers. It is very useful for all agents to understand what kind of top performance is capable of being achieved.

Once you have identified struggling agents, reinforce the people-centered environment you have attempted to create. Agents like Sam will feel threatened. Privately review with them individually that the resources of the contact center are going to be at their disposal so that skills can be improved over time. Remind them that real improvement will only come if they apply themselves during the supplemental training. If you believe, like I do, that poor performances are seldom caused by bad attitudes then the source of poor performance must be holes in the skills and knowledge that the top performers possess. This brings the re-engineering team to its next significant task, the creation of a skill and knowledge inventory.

Skill and Knowledge Set

Visiting hundreds of contact centers over the years provides a real respect for the job an agent performs. In the vast majority of contact centers, an agent's role is complex and difficult. A very large and diverse skill and knowledge set is required before an agent masters the job. Mastery is defined as the ability to achieve acceptable levels of performance (productivity and quality) without excessive effort or stress—nothing superhuman.

A very useful re-engineering team discussion, perhaps lasting several sessions, can revolve around identifying the skill and knowledge inventory— the things an agent must possess to achieve mastery. It is useful to let the re-engineering team attempt to define this list. If they have trouble or are not using the time well, it is beneficial to provide a starting point. Some centers gravitate towards the following high-level skill and knowledge inventory:

1. Listening skills
2. Courtesy and telephone etiquette
3. Speaking skills
4. Call control skills
5. Typing skills
6. Telephone and computer manipulation skills
7. Products and services knowledge

8. Policy and procedure knowledge

9. Handling difficult callers skills

At times some of these skills can merge into a single category. occasionally, the re-engineering team wants the basic list to be larger and more comprehensive. Some teams decide to put attitude elements into the inventory.

Once the high-level list is in place, it is important to provide some detail for each category. The trainers, supervisors, or both will require as much detail as possible for reasons that will be clear in just a bit.

A detailed skill inventory is required for one reason. The Quality/Productivity chart identifies agents, like Sam, who appear to be struggling with both elements of their job. Once they have been identified, it is the responsibility of the contact center management to help them improve.

The process to accomplish this is to use additional silent monitoring, side-by-side monitoring, recordings and even peer monitoring to focus on the precise skill and knowledge deficiencies. The best results can be obtained if the quality monitor records some of Sam's conversations. Setting aside some quiet time, the quality monitor listens carefully to the recorded conversation and evaluates the call against each inventory item. Focusing, the monitor can begin to identify at a detail level what skills and knowledge Sam seems to lack. After doing this for several different calls, the quality monitor will begin to develop a sense of Sam's deficiencies. Side-by-side monitoring sessions, where the monitor plugs into Sam's set, will further sharpen the assessment. The side-by-side monitoring will also reveal mechanical problems, if they exist. This refers to keyboard difficulties, computer desktop navigation problems or telephone set manipulation problems.

A powerful aid for struggling agents is to let them listen to recordings of their own calls. This is particularly true if they seem to be having problems with quality components. If the re-engineering team has reached an agreement to do peer reviews, agents like Sam can greatly benefit from listening to high-performing agents.

Retraining of struggling agents is a difficult task. It is not appropriate to simply recycle these agents through new-hire training. That is very demotivating and adversely impacts self-esteem. It is not indicative of a people-centered environment. Instead, focused training packages must be created and made available. A real example highlights this important point. The Quality/Productivity chart (used as an illustration in this section) contains data from a real contact center. Sam is a real agent. After identifying that Sam was struggling, his supervisor used both skills and knowledge monitoring, as well as side-by-side monitoring. Sam's critical problem was that he was a very poor touch-typist. As a result, his transaction time was longer than it should have been owing to the slow typing rate and the errors introduced by hitting the wrong keys. With a lot of his attention directed towards typing, Sam also displayed some of the characteristics of poor listening. The typing deficiency affected productivity primarily although a secondary effect rippled through the quality issues.

The focused training program created for Sam consisted of a PC-based typing course. This package permitted him to sign off the system during low traffic periods to take a self-paced typing drills course. In addition, Sam was given taped recordings of his own calls. He was encouraged to listen to them with the supervisor and discuss what elements of the call were good and which needed some improvement. After four months, Sam had moved up the Q/P chart significantly. He is approaching the Deming bands for both criteria, and is one of the most loyal and enthusiastic agents that the contact center has in their employ.

Recognition and Motivation

While the primary purpose of the Quality/Productivity chart is to identify struggling agents so that scarce resources can be allocated appropriately, there are other equally important uses. One of the more important applications is in the area of motivation, recognition and rewards.

Everyone requires motivation occasionally, even so-called self-motivating people. We are all subject to the normal vicissitudes of life. Some days we just don't feel up to the challenge. Sometimes we can pull ourselves together and perform our tasks with the usual vigor.

One of the difficulties described earlier had to do with the challenges associated with motivating agents. Contact center management can engage in two very different kinds of motivation. First, the manager has to be concerned with motivating the "oldtimers." The experienced agents are most likely the ones with the highest productivity and quality. These agents need to remain productive. Management needs superstars to hold up in front of the rest of the agent population as role models. On a more prosaic level, management needs high performers to keep on performing so that the productivity of the center doesn't slide.

The second kind of motivation management must engage in has to do with incentivizing new hires to move as rapidly through the training curve as is possible. It is quite natural to expect less from a new hire than an experienced agent. But when does an agent cross the boundary between new hire and experienced agent? Is it purely a matter of time on the job or is it more a matter of learning and doing? One thing that can be said with certainty is that the contact center would be better off if new hires became productive sooner rather than later. So the question reduces to how management practices can speed up the process. Happily, the

Quality/Productivity chart can play a major role in resolving the issues surrounding agent motivation.

A mistake that some contact centers make is to create an agent-of-the month award. Frequently, this award is conferred upon a single agent each month. The process used to select the winner is typically one where the supervisors and manager meet monthly, each with a candidate for the award. Conversation among the supervisors, guided by the manager, is supposed to identify the most deserving agent. There are many problems with this approach. First, it is entirely subjective. Second, supervisors with good argumentation skills can sway opinions towards their agent nominee. Third, agents have no clear concept regarding the criteria used to select the winner. How can they model their behaviors? Lastly, these kinds of recognitions frequently degrade into pseudo-popularity contests. Agents with outgoing personalities, whom everyone likes, are much more likely to receive supervisor consensus. Although agent-of-the-month awards seem to devolve into demotivators, at least these centers are trying, even if their efforts are misguided. A story illustrates how this happens.

One contact center had a typical employee-of-the-month award. As luck would have it, one of the senior agents in the center had a very outgoing personality. During one six-month period this agent was nominated for the award and won three times. While this was going on, management noticed that morale in the center seemed to be declining. In fact, some agents seemed to be growing rude to callers. This problem continued to grow until management discovered that one of the sources of all this was the senior agent himself. Whenever this agent was confronted with an angry caller he asked if they would prefer to speak with his supervisor. Most of the angry callers were only too glad to have this choice and agreed to be transferred to a supervisor. Then the agent would routinely say, "Just a moment while I transfer you to Mr. Click." And then he would promptly hang up on the caller! This routine was overheard by a few agents sitting nearby and quickly became the subject of conversation among all the agents. Bestowing the employee-of-the-month award on the same agent had the effect of shattering morale and generating negative behaviors among other agents.

One of the more common mistakes made in contact centers has to do with recognition—there isn't any. The next most common mistake is that although there is some recognition and reward, it is viewed by the agent population as being administered unfairly.

In many contact centers there is no established recognition and reward program. When queried, most of the managers in these centers claimed that the company provided no budget for this incentive. The unstated assumption is that recognition and reward equates to money. Establishing incentives is very important and requires some funds, but not nearly as much as most managers believe.

Because the contact center is an invisible world, simple recognition of high performers can be a powerful motivator. One of the principles of successful contact center management is to make agent performance visible. If you have been fortunate enough to receive approval from the re-engineering team to post the Quality/Productivity chart in the contact center, then recognition has begun. The superstars will be recognized for their accomplishments by both management and their peers. Management can dramatize the effect of the public posting and accompanying recognition without spending a great deal of money. For example, in one contact center the superstars' cubicles are bedecked with helium-filled balloons when a new Q/P chart is published. The balloons cost very little, yet they draw attention, add color and provide a focus for conversation. The last item might be the most important. Be vigilant about seizing every opportunity to break down the natural formation of cliques and factions among the agent population. Providing circumstances that encourage conversation among agents helps to break down barriers and builds a sense of teamwork.

Don't overlook congratulatory letters from senior management as a motivator and display of recognition. More contact centers are establishing "walls of honor" where complimentary letters from customers and senior management are displayed. Both kinds of letters are important. Letters of praise from customers are particularly prized since this is at the heart of the very reason for instituting a contact center. Letters from senior management reaffirm for all the agents that what they do on a daily basis is recognized and appreciated by executives.

Recognition should flow to agents who inhabit the upper right-hand quadrant of the Q/P Matrix. These agents are the high performers without whose efforts the contact center would not be able to sustain the existing service level. The Q/P chart can also be used to recognize and motivate new hires. There are two different ways the chart can be used for this purpose. Some contact centers create defined classes of agent. For example, one contact center classifies new-hires as agents with less than six months tenure; tenure greater than six months, but less than one year are junior agents; and tenure over one year are senior agents. They have created productivity and quality goals for each of the three classifications. Each class of agent has its own Q/P Matrix. Thus, each class has its own superstars.

A second way to use the Q/P Matrix to motivate new hires and trainees is by calculating and tracking what we call the "Figure of Merit." The Figure of Merit is a number that dimensions the distance between two Q/P chart points.

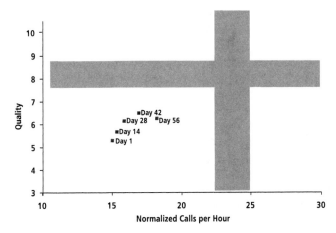

Figure 6-14. Individual Q/P Chart & Figure of Merit

In the above example, the Figure of Merit can be calculated by using the following formula:

Figure of Merit = $(Q_2-Q_1) + (P_2-P_1)$

where Q_1, P_1 represent the scores on the first date and Q_2, P_2 are the scores on the last date. In the example above, the first score pair (5.3,15) is day 1 and the last score pair (6.5,18.3) is day 56. The calculation is as follows:

Figure of Merit = (6.5 - 5.3) + (18.3 - 15)
                = (1.3) + (3.3)
                = 4.6

Recognition is provided for agents who have the largest Figure of Merit over a set period of time.

It was mentioned earlier that some interesting results could be obtained if you make a perfect quality score equal to the highest theoretic normalized productivity score. When quality scores are set this way, the Figure of Merit score will be balanced between productivity and quality. In the example, the Figure of Merit calculation places a greater emphasis upon productivity. Some contact centers solve this calculation problem by using a multiplier on the change in quality score. In the example, since a perfect productivity score is 30 while a perfect quality score is 10, use a multiplier of 3 on the quality scores.

A useful policy for Figure of Merit calculations is that there can be no negative quality changes. That is, if over the time frame of the Figure of Merit period an agent improves in productivity but declines in quality then their Figure of Merit is automatically zero. This rule tends to drive the center towards quality over pure productivity.

How recognition is manifested depends upon the prevailing or desired culture in that contact center. The culture of a contact center is frequently a function of the manager's personality. Where the manager is reserved and retiring, the center's culture often reflects this and manifests itself with notions of professionalism and decorum. Where the manager is outgoing and accessible, the center's culture is often less restrictive and more playful. There is no such a thing as *the* right culture for a contact center. Great contact centers exist with very different cultures. Perhaps the best piece of advice that can be offered on this minor issue is that the manager should not attempt to create a culture that is inconsistent with his or her own personality. If you tend to view yourself as the consummate professional, a no-nonsense manager, then attempts at creating an open, slightly irreverent, fun atmosphere will likely fail.

Contests

Unfortunately, contests seem to have fallen from favor as a means of motivating the agent population. Contests can be an important element in the ongoing quest for world-class contact center status. The reasons why contests are not used in more contact centers have to do with the usual problems. Frequently, contests fail to achieve the desired results because of the way they are set up and the length of time they run.

Contests that have only one or, at best, a few winners have the potential to demotivate agents. This is particularly true when the contest winner is the agent with the highest productivity. At the outset of such a contest, new-hires and trainees will recognize that they do not have a chance to win. To avoid this problem, use agent classifications with prizes in each class or use more complex contest criteria involving Figure of Merit.

One contact center solved their contest problems by using Figure of Merit and the Q/P Matrix without resorting to agent classification. First, the management sought and received approval to create a grab bag of prizes. The prizes included:
- A day off with pay
- Dinner for two
- One evening at a bed and breakfast
- $50 cash award

To promote the idea that anyone could win, the contact center management seized upon the idea of drawing names from a hat. The contest rules determined how agents got their names into the hat.

The contest time frame was two months; the Q/P Matrix was the centerpiece. On March 1st a Q/P chart was prepared according to schedule. This chart served as the baseline chart. The final chart would be used to determine whose names were in the drawing and how many chances each agent would receive. This gave all the agents an opportunity to work towards prize qualification. On March 15th, the first contest Q/P chart was produced. The rules of the contest described various ways that agents could get slips of paper with their names placed into the prize drawing. The rules were:

Final Dot in Superstar Quadrant	– 3 Chances
Final Dot in Deming Band	– 2 Chances
Figure of Merit . . . .>4	– 5 Chances
. . . . .2<x<4	– 3 Chances
. . . . .1<x<2	– 2 Chances
. . . . .0<x<1	– 1 Chance

Under these rules it is possible for an agent to get as many as 8 chances to win a prize. An agent who had a Figure of Merit improvement of greater than 4 units and who ended up in the superstar quadrant would get 8 chances.

This is an outstanding approach to judging a contest. It recognizes that superstars are important. It also recognizes that agents who meet Deming band standards are fully contributing. And, it recognizes new agents who are achieving improvements in their performance. The drawing element adds randomness to the outcome. This helps ensure that the winners won't be exclusively oldtimers. This kind of contest has been executed with great success in contact centers.

The contest should have a theme. Amazingly, any theme seems to do. There is no such thing as too corny. Choosing a theme seems to give the agent population an immediate lift. In one case, the re-engineering team decided to use a baseball theme featuring the supervisors as "coaches." This theme was used to reinforce the entire Quality and Productivity management process. Portraying the supervisors as coaches dedicated to helping the agents master their jobs, underscored management's commitment towards creating a world-class contact center.

Rewards

What a pity that the concept of "reward" has become increasingly, almost exclusively, linked with money in our culture. For this reason, reward systems are almost nonexistent in most contact centers. Oh, salaries are reviewed according to company policy and likely some performance criteria are considered. But a real reward system is much more than annual salary reviews. A wide-ranging, well-executed reward system is a powerful motivator and a performance-enhancing technique in the hands of the quality monitors and management.

One of the more dramatic implementations of the Q/P Matrix is to associate wage premiums with quadrant occupancy. For example, consider the following: the lower left quadrant is a baseline pay rate; occupancy in one Deming band is some percentage premium, such as 5%; occupancy in both Deming bands is 10%; and occupancy in the upper right quadrant is 15%.

Other rewards are less dramatic. Frequently, contests feature cash prizes. Employee-of-the-month recognition sometimes carries a small cash award. Cash prizes can be used to good effect in contests and reward systems, but they should be kept small. It is easy to let cash prizes escalate over time to keep interest moving up. Large cash awards tend to evoke isolating behaviors among the contestants because the common perception is that there are large stakes at hand. Smaller cash awards of less than $50 (and, more commonly, $25) don't interfere with teaming behaviors.

Some rewards to consider for your inventory have already been mentioned. An overnight bed and breakfast award can be relatively inexpensive. Dinner for two can be defined as not to exceed a certain dollar value, such as $50. A lunch prize can be created for less than $10. Time off is a very desirable award. Check with accounting on this issue, some organizations have very strict rules regarding attendance, payroll and taxes. If you have managerial prerogative, time off is probably easier to arrange.

Many contact centers use very small awards to reinforce desirable behaviors. In one center the quality monitors had tokens that could be redeemed for highly valued cookies in the cafeteria. Whenever a quality monitor heard a noteworthy, excellent conversation, they would immediately walk over to the agent and award a cookie token with great fanfare. This kind of small, simple reward is perhaps the most effective.

What About Outbound?

The management processes suggested here are designed specifically for the pure (or almost pure) inbound contact center. A legitimate question is: What about outbound contact centers? Don't we need similar management tools? In a word, yes. However, the orientation ought to be different.

While it makes lots of sense to measure the number of calls handled in the inbound contact center, it does not make sense to measure the number of calls placed outbound. Why? While an inbound center's reason for existence is to handle incoming calls, an outbound center exists to obtain an outcome from the call. Usually the desired outcome of an outbound call is for the party called to agree to an action. The action might be to place an order, complete a survey or to make an appointment with a company representative.

Systems designed to automate outbound dialing provide a number of measures that are more important and revealing than just the number of calls placed. Quality issues are still important, very important. But some criteria other than calls placed needs to be positioned against the quality scores. Consider using dollars sold, appointments secured, surveys completed, pledges accepted or any outcome-oriented measurement. Everything else in the management processes can remain the same.

Blended Centers

A growing trend in contact centers is to use some agents in a "blended" environment. That is, some agents are capable of handling incoming calls and conducting outbound call campaigns. Years ago there were debates in the industry as to whether inbound agents could be successful when making outbound telemarketing calls, and whether successful outbound telemarketers could adapt to handling routine, predictable, incoming calls. The debate was pointless.

It was probably to be expected that a lot of contact centers went ahead and tried "blended agents." The rationale behind this concept is straightforward. Even in well-run inbound contact centers there will be periods of the day when inbound agents exceed the inbound call demand. If these periods are lengthy, it makes sense to send some agents home to avoid unnecessary labor expense. But if these periods of slack inbound call volume are relatively short (say 30 minutes here and 30 minutes there), it probably makes better sense to find something else for the surplus agents to do. This provides some productivity for the organization and keeps them on hand to start taking calls again when required. A good use for some surplus agent time is to make outbound telemarketing calls.

Use the inbound management charts as depicted here. The normalizing function can be used but you will need to subtract all the time allocated to outbound calling. Use the appropriate outbound measurements for the time the agent spends doing that task.

Performance Metrics for Multimedia Transactions

The first thing that can be said with some certainty is that we are all in a learning mode. Happily, we don't have to start from a blank sheet of paper. Call centers have been worrying about metrics for years and have created some useful measures. At minimum, contact centers will likely adapt some of the same metrics used to report voice transactions for multimedia transactions.

Because so many call centers are pure customer service centers, a good deal of thinking has been applied to the lack of a link between customer service and the value associated with customer retention. It is clear that retaining a customer is more cost-effective than winning over a new customer. And it is equally clear that the lifetime revenue stream of a retained customer is much higher than from customers who "flow" through an enterprise in a matter of a few years. Some effort has been made to quantify the impact of customer service, but these efforts are aimed at the enterprise level and do not lend themselves to individual agent metrics. This must be the case because it is seemingly impossible to project future revenue stream differences owing to the outcome of a single call center interaction.

To this problem we now add the impact of multimedia. It is probably unwise to lump the various communication modalities that comprise new media into a single category. For our purposes, new media could be broken down into e-mail handling and Web assistance.

I maintain that at the top level, familiar metrics will do nicely for e-mail. That is: We will be interested in knowing the total number of such trans-actions by time of day, average handling (or transaction) time, time in queue before handling and some disposition coding (e.g., What was the outcome?). Obviously, we will want to have a report indicating how well the application was executed against the service level goal. It will be useful to know how much agent labor is being expended.

At the agent level, things will be more difficult. When an e-mail message is routed to an agent for handling, it might be necessary for the agent to acquire information not readily at hand. Requests for information might go out to other functional groupings in the enterprise or even outside the enterprise altogether. Time will pass before the needed data is furnished to the agent. Is it useful to know that 17 hours elapsed before the agent was able to furnish a reply? Would it be useful to know that of those 17 hours, 16.8 hours was spent waiting for replies to agent-initiated questions? Is it more useful to know that when all the needed data was finally in the agent's possession, the reply took 2 minutes to write? Is it useful to know that the reply was scored an 11.7 on the Flesch-Kincaid Grade Level Score? In fact, all of these metrics are useful. My opinion is that a combination of a time metric or metrics and readability score will prove to be most useful.

Happily, Microsoft Word already provides the readability scoring. We should be prepared to adopt that metric into e-mail agent reporting. One way to do that would be to sample e-mail replies from each agent. Pass the text through the Microsoft Word Spelling and Grammar routine found under the Tools menu. Along with spelling and basic grammar flags, Microsoft Word produces two readability scores: Flesch-Kincaid Grade Level Score and the Flesch Reading Ease score. From the Microsoft Word Help Index we are informed that each readability score bases its rating on the average number of syllables per word and words per sentence. The Flesch Reading Ease score rates text on a 100-point scale. The higher the score, the easier it is to understand the document. For most standard documents, the writer is encouraged to aim for a score of approximately 60 to 70. The Flesch-Kincaid Grade Level score rates text on a U.S. grade-school level. For example, a score of 8.0 means that an eighth grader can understand the document. For most standard documents, the writer is encouraged to aim for a score of approximately 7.0 to 8.0. I ran this paragraph through the spelling and grammar checker tool and it informed me that the Flesch Reading Ease score for this paragraph is 55.9 and the Flesch-Kincaid Grade Level score for the paragraph is 9.3. If this were an e-mail response and the contact center adopted the recommendations provided by Microsoft Word Help, I would be encouraged to use shorter sentences.

Web-assistance transactions represent a different challenge. Today, a voice call is a continuous event that starts with hello and ends with goodbye. Web-assistance transactions are likely to more closely resemble how customers and store clerks interact in a physical-shopping environment. Consider the following typical encounter. A customer strolls into the store. They walk about for awhile, looking here and there. When they have a question, they approach a store clerk, ask the question, get a reply and then either disengage from the clerk or ask more questions. This solitary shopping by wandering around is interspersed with questions and conversational interchanges with various store clerks until the customer buys something or leaves. If we replace the store with a Web site and store clerks with Web-enabled agents, the analogy holds. How will we judge performance of our Web-enabled agents? They are likely to have lots and lots of short interchanges with multiple shoppers. Sometimes an item will be purchased. We've already seen that metrics that focus upon revenue are not particularly worthwhile at the individual agent level. In fact, since we have all shopped in our lives, don't we easily recognize shops where too much emphasis has been placed on making the sale? Don't we judge the store clerks as too pushy or overbearing? In a virtual store, a shopper can leave an overbearing, revenue-hungry agent behind with a single mouse-click. It appears that the most useful metric will be a subjective quality measurement. Did the agent follow enterprise policy and procedure? And, did they do the transaction with a smile?

When we turn to productivity measures for Web site support, things get murkier. If my speculation is accurate that a Web site visitor might interact with several different agents during their stay or that a Web site visitor might return to the site several times before making a purchase, then it is difficult, maybe impossible, to relate an agent interaction to a specific purchase. The same problems pertain in retail brick-and-mortar stores. We may be forced to measure productivity on a group basis and rely entirely upon quality monitoring processes to identify agents who might need supplemental training in dealing with Web site support transactions.

Chapter 7:
Managing Cost per Transaction

A song in the hit play *Cabaret* tells us that "money makes the world go 'round." They might as well be singing about contact centers. There are thousands of applications and scores of equipment approaches you can consider, and although each of these has its own revenue, service and cost implications, they all share one common denominator: cost per transaction.

Every organization knows their cost per transaction. This is an incorrect assumption. Simply, most don't know how to determine it. Of course, you can't begin to manage something unless you can measure it. Here's how to calculate this key figure.

A typical contact center has three cost components: labor, technology and transmission. To simplify, include the cost of facilities and other labor-related expenses in the labor costs.

Calculating the labor component is fairly straightforward but recognize that some of the labor cost in a contact center is indirect. Technology cost includes allowances for ACD system costs, computer system costs and the furniture used in the contact center. Transmission costs are those associated with inbound and outbound calling and any allocated expenses associated with the local area network, e-mail and Web site systems.

Determining Labor Costs

This is the easiest management cost to determine, although it might require a little legwork and persistence. Essentially, the information required is how much each person in the contact center is paid and how their time is allocated by the nature of the transaction. As in the productivity measurements, it is suggested that cost-per-transaction calculations be performed with data spanning at least one week's operations. Keep track of who worked, for how many hours and at what task. Most contact center systems can readily provide this kind of information. If the center technology is not fully integrated you might have to deal with multiple databases and take some extra effort to develop this metric. At a minimum, the ACD reports will provide on-phone time for all agents and supervisors. Depending upon the contact center policy, time allocated to breaks and lunches may or may not appear on the ACD report. All paid time must be reflected in the report or else adjust the numbers accordingly. Acquire salary data for each agent if it isn't already available. Discuss with Human Resources or Personnel the cost of fringe benefits in your company and how to factor in for this expense.

An example of the data that can be extracted from an ACD report and necessary data obtained from Personnel is arranged here:

Agent Name	Hours	Rate	Extension	Benefit	Total
Smith, Kevin	40	$10.50	$ 420.00	1.35	$ 567.00
Jones, Mary	40	11.25	450.00	1.35	607.50
Maloney, Bob	40	9.50	380.00	1.35	513.00
Williams, Janet	30	8.75	262.50	1.20	315.00
Clancy, Nancy	40	10.25	410.00	1.35	553.50
Dodd, Laura	25	7.85	196.25	1.20	235.50
Perkins, Sam	17	7.50	127.50	1.20	153.00
Ryan, William	40	9.75	390.00	1.35	526.50
Cage, Donna	40	11.00	440.00	1.35	594.00
Sea, Stormy	20	8.25	165.00	1.20	198.00
Baker, Susan	40	11.50	460.00	1.35	621.00
Bonnetti, Cindy	22	8.50	187.00	1.20	224.40
Chase, Margo	18	8.25	148.50	1.20	178.20
Hoopster, Karol	24	7.75	186.00	1.20	223.20
Totals	436		$4,222.75		$5,509.80

The "Benefit" column represents a multiplier factor that transforms gross pay into the actual employee cost as experienced by the company. This multiplier factor reflects the employer portion of FICA, health benefits and other contributions entirely or partially borne by the company.

Do not overlook the people who are not agents but who work on behalf of the contact center. The most obvious additions are supervisors and the contact center manager. Clerical help, training personnel and technical personnel associated with the contact center are sometimes overlooked.

In the example above, fourteen people are listed in the labor cost chart. Consider a manager and a clerical person as necessary additions to our small contact center. Likely all 14 people are not all on the phones at the same time. Some of the part-time agents fill in coverage during breaks, lunches and other routine activities that take away from call handling time. For purposes of the example, assume that contact center management and indirect employees add $1,000 to the weekly labor cost figure above. Thus, the total cost of direct and indirect labor in the cost-per-transaction example is $6,509.80.

Facilities Costs

Operation of a contact center involves certain physical facilities that must considered to identify the real operational costs of the contact center. Among the things to consider in facilities costs are the floor space, power, heating, cooling, etc. Without going into a massive pro rata analysis of known corporate expenses, ask Personnel or Accounting for a per-square-foot cost figure that includes all these items.

The example has 14 agent workstations, a manager's office, a clerical station and necessary common areas like aisles, break rooms, and so on. It is pretty easy to calculate the amount of space that the contact center operation consumes. Don't forget the associated space, especially the break area. Carrying the example forward, consider the following calculations:

Agent workstations 14 @ 36 sq. ft. each	504 sq. ft.
Manager's office	80
Clerical station	64
Break room	140
Common areas (aisles, etc.)	300
Total	1,088 sq. ft.

If Accounting provides a figure of $16 per square foot as the annual facilities costs, then the total annual facilities costs will be $17,408. A contact center is likely open 52 weeks a year, so the weekly facilities cost is $334.77.

Supplies

This category includes forms, manila folders, paper, pens, pencils, coffee, cups and all the various items that people use endlessly whenever work is performed. You may already track these kinds of expenses through a miscellaneous expense account. Don't spend a lot of time trying to identify these costs too carefully. In our example situation assume these costs total $25 per week.

Technology Costs

Most contact centers include a telephone system for voice processing, a computer system (either a mainframe/terminal configuration or personal computers linked into a local area network) and furniture for the telephone representatives. Obviously, your contact center may also include IVR, voice mail, workforce management software, and so on.

You need to know the cost of the various systems and the cost of software support and maintenance for each. If you want to be precise about these costs, either calculate the Net Present Value of the maintenance payments or ask Accounting to do this for you. Net Present Value calculations take into account that a future maintenance payment of $100 really only costs about $94 today. Another way of thinking about this is to realize that if you put $94 in a savings account today, next year you would have $100 available after interest, to pay next year's maintenance. Nearly all spreadsheet programs have an embedded Net Present Value function. All you need to know is how the imbedded function likes to see the data and the assumption about interest rates.

After you calculate the purchase price and Net Present Value of the maintenance payments, you have the total cost of the contact center systems expressed in today's dollars. Then, divide this figure by the expected life of the system (sometimes called the useful life) to determine annual and weekly technology costs.

To illustrate this step, let's make a few assumptions. First, let's say the cost of the ACD system is $3,500 per position. Since the example has 14 positions, the cost of the ACD system is $49,000. The annual maintenance cost for the ACD system is $5,000. The maintenance and software support for the first year is included in the purchase price but subsequent years are an additional expense. If the useful life of the ACD system is 5 years, the future payment situation is depicted below:

	Year 1	Year 2	Year 3	Year 4	Year 5
Install ACD	$49,000				
Maintenance		$5,000	$5,000	$5,000	$5,000

Assuming an interest rate of 6%, the Net Present Value of the maintenance payments is $17,325.53. The total cost of the ACD system is the sum of the purchase price and the net present value of the maintenance payments. In the example, the total cost for the ACD system is $66,325.53. The annual cost of the ACD system over its 5-year useful life is $13,265.11, and the weekly cost turns out to be $255.10.

The next item under Technology Costs involves the computer system. A rigorous approach would force us to place a value upon the application software being used in each workstation. While it is easy to value purchased software, it is not so easy to value internally developed software. Assuming that each agent in the contact center is equipped with a multimedia PC linked to a local area network, computer costs can be pegged at roughly $3,000 per agent. The software costs are purely speculative. For purposes of this illustration, the per-workstation software costs are estimated to be an additional $5,000. It wouldn't be a surprise if some agent workstation software costs exceed $15,000 per position.

The computer hardware and software costs are $8,000 per workstation. The 14-position center has a total computer cost of $112,000. Using the same useful life of 5 years that was employed for the ACD system yields an annual cost of $22,400, and a weekly cost of $430.77.

The last item under Technology is perhaps arbitrary—furniture. It is easier to consider furniture along with ACD and computer costs because all are workstation oriented. Furniture expense covers a broad range of costs. It is possible to establish a small contact center with lunch tables for desks. At the other extreme, modular furniture available from several national sources typically can cost from $2,000 to $4,000 per workstation. The cost of furniture is set at $3,000 per workstation for purposes of this illustration and has a useful life of 5 years. The total cost of the furniture is $42,000. Therefore, the annual cost is $8,400, and the weekly cost is $161.54.

Transmission Cost

The final component to consider in contact center costs is transmission costs. These are the most variable of all costs. Many contact centers, especially those whose reach is local, use regular business lines where the calling party bears the expense of the call. To be fair, even these business lines cost the contact center manager something. It is understood, however, that most contact centers will use In-Wats or free-phone circuits where the caller bears no cost.

There are two ways to approach this cost element. One, you can use the actual bill that is received from the service provider. The only problem with this approach is that you must wait for the bill to be received before you do any cost-per-transaction calculations for the previous month. While old data is better than no data, month-old cost-per-transaction information is ancient history. The second way is to develop a cost per minute associated with the In-Wats billing, whose In-Wats rates have been declining for some time. Obviously, large users enjoy lower per-minute rates owing to their bargaining power, economies of scale and volume. If you cannot identify your In-Wats charges or calculate your own per-minute rate, you could probably use an estimated rate of $.15 per minute and achieve fair accuracy.

Cost-per-Transaction Recap

The following costs have been expressed as weekly operating costs:

Labor (direct and indirect)	$6,509.80
Facilities	334.77
Supplies	25.00
ACD costs	255.10
Computer costs	430.77
Furniture	161.54
Subtotal	$7,716.98

And, one cost (transmission) is expressed as a per-minute rate of $.15.

The final step in this process is to examine a traffic report from the ACD system for the week just ended. Almost all systems will report the final two required pieces of data: the total trunk occupancy time and the total number of calls handled for the week. Special note for managers of blended centers: Don't forget to consider outbound calling costs. Some outbound calls are placed in support of and directly associated with servicing inbound calls. Include those costs with your calculations for inbound cost per transaction. You probably should discover and use a different cost per minute for outbound calling because it is usually less expensive than the free-phone In-Wats charges. If you have separate outbound telemarketing campaigns, exclude these costs when calculating inbound cost per transaction. The total trunk occupancy time is needed in order to derive the total transmission costs for the week. Don't make the mistake of considering only talk time. When using In-Wats circuits, you also pay for queue time. That is why the total trunk occupancy time is needed since that figure will include all the time callers wait in queue on the In-Wats circuits.

For the purposes of the example, the ACD report for the week ended indicates that the total In-Wats trunk occupancy time is 8,450 minutes. Use the per-minute rate to calculate the weekly In-Wats transmission costs. The weekly transmission costs work out to be $1,267.50. Add this figure to the weekly costs calculated earlier to produce the following:

Labor, Direct and Indirect	$6,509.80
Facilities	334.77
Supplies	25.00
ACD Costs	255.10
Computer Costs	430.77
Furniture	161.54
Transmission Costs	1,267.50
Total	$8,984.48

The last step in the process consists of using the number of calls actually handled during the week to divide into the total costs calculated above. The cost-per-transaction example is completed when the weekly report reveals that 2,600 calls were offered and 2,444 were actually handled.

Doing the math yields the cost per transaction. In the example, the cost per transaction is $8,761.17 divided by 2,444 calls or $3.68 per transaction.

After calculating the cost per transaction, it might be useful to compare the cost components to the total:

	Dollars per Week	Percent of Total
Labor		
Labor and benefits	$6,509.80	72.5%
Facilities	334.77	3.7%
Supplies	25.00	0.3%
Subtotal	$6,869.57	76.5%
Technology		
ACD system	$255.10	2.8%
Computer system	430.77	4.8%
Furniture	161.54	1.8%
Subtotal	$847.41	9.4%
Transmission costs		
In-Wats trunks	$1,267.50	14.1%

Determining the cost per transaction and the relationship of cost components to the total cost are very useful exercises. If you are a revenue center where each call has an expected average revenue value, the cost-per-transaction information will let you quickly determine the contact center's "gross profit." If you are a pure customer service center and nobody is willing or able to suggest what each call is worth in customer retention and loyalty, at least you have a cost-per-transaction figure to work against.

One lesson is made painfully obvious: To control contact center costs, it is much more rewarding to focus on labor and transmission costs than to worry about relatively small technology costs. Archimedes said several thousand years ago that if someone gave him a lever big enough and a place to stand, that he could move the earth. Similarly, in a contact center your lever and place to stand is technology. With the right tools you can move cost per transaction downward. It would seem evident that buying the best tools, even if premium prices must be paid, is a justifiable behavior for contact center managers.

Cost-per-Transaction Dynamics

An interesting exercise involves reviewing cost per transaction with your superiors. It is particularly powerful just before budget time. Instead of calculating all the costs that are borne in a contact center, look at just the really variable costs per transaction. Focus on labor and transmission costs.

Using the example, recall that the average agent labor costs were $12.64 per hour. This result is obtained by dividing the total labor cost of $5,509.80 by the total labor hours figure of 436. The cost of transmission is $.15 per minute. An average half-hour period in the contact center sees 65 call attempts. The average talk time is 180 seconds and the average after-call work time is 15 seconds. The Erlang staffing program was run several times to produce the following table of data:

Agents Staffed	ASA	DLYDLY	Service Level	Occupancy	Callers Waiting > 90 Seconds
8	132.0	203.5	41.2%	88%	27
9	39.3	99.6	67.7%	78%	10
10	15.0	65.9	83%	70%	4
11	6.2	49.3	91.7%	64%	1
12	2.6	39.3	96.1%	59%	0

If an assumption is made that no callers are willing to wait longer than 90 seconds (not wholly unreasonable), then another array of data can be produced as follows:

Agents Staffed	Half-Hour Labor Cost	Transmission Minutes	Cost	Calls Answered	Cost per Call
8	$50.56	338	$50.70	38	$2.66
9	56.88	229.5	34.43	55	1.66
10	63.20	211.25	31.69	61	1.555
11	69.52	201.7	30.25	64	1.558
12	75.84	197.8	29.67	65	1.62

The interesting thing about this set of data is that it illustrates several points made earlier in this book. Plotted here are the variable costs per call. This is a useful figure since there is little anyone can do about floor space, technology and computer costs. What you do get faced with from time to time is a management request to reduce labor headcount as a means of reducing overall expense.

Forget service level. Forget average speed of answer. Let's focus on cost per transaction. If we staff this particular half-hour with 8 agents, our variable cost per transaction answered will be $2.66. At the other extreme, if we staff the half-hour with 12 agents, our variable cost per transaction answered will be $1.62. The minimum variable cost per transaction in practical terms is obtained using either 10 or 11 staffed agent positions. What is interesting about this contact center example is that if the absolute minimum variable cost-per-transaction option is used, you deliver pretty good service. The service level is 83%. Also, notice that the agent occupancy is just 70%. Nearly one-third of the time, agents are waiting for the next caller.

Attacking Cost-per-Transaction

Suppose you have just calculated your contact center's cost per transaction and after the heart palpitations diminish somewhat, you resolve to slash cost per transaction. What would you do? How would you attack the problem? Here's one approach.

Step One: conduct a series of meetings with everybody in the contact center. Explain what the problem is (high costs, poor quality, low productivity, too many abandons, etc.) and why it is important to solve it. Make this session educational in nature. There is a high probability that some agents will feel threatened the minute you mention costs. Most, however, will be quick enough to determine that agent payroll is the largest expense and that, therefore, personal trouble lies ahead. Stress that cost per transaction can be reduced in many different ways that have nothing to do with reducing headcount (as will be seen).

The outcome of these meetings should be to form a team that will act as a conduit between the agent force and management. Call it an Operations Team. When considering the team's makeup, keep diversity firmly in mind. Access to all the groups and factions that tend to form in any group of people is required. Ideas, recommendations, requests for information and similar input will move through this team. An equally important function for the team is to act as an information exchange mechanism. As ideas are discussed in the Operations Team, they should be discussed among the entire agent force in informal settings—during breaks and lunches, for example. The team members should also serve as a lightning rod for the agent force. Attitudes, emotions and feelings are important and require ventilation. The Operations Team is the right mechanism to achieve these goals.

Step Two: gather at least one week's worth of data. Produce as many charts from Chapter 6 as you can. The reports will suggest further activities that will be discussed shortly.

Step Three: if you do not use wrap-up call coding, now's the time to implement it. Work with the team to define all the transaction types that come into your contact center. In a banking customer service application we might develop a call transaction type list that includes the following:

Bank Customer Service Call Types
- Balance requests
- Statement questions
- Change of address

- Product inquiry
- Rate inquiry
- Funds transfer request
- Stop payment request
- Lost/stolen checkbook
- Merchant call, check clear indication
- Merchant call, credit check
- Automatic Teller Machine problem

The reason this kind of information is needed is that one way to reduce cost per transaction is to substitute an inexpensive answer mechanism for a relatively more expensive one. Before considering tactics along these lines, you have to know what you are dealing with in terms of transaction types and the number of occurrences of each.

If your system has a wrap-up recording feature, this is an easy data collection task to implement. You can assign numeric codes to each call type. Most ACD systems will not only count the number of occurrences of each code but will track the talk time and after-call work time as well. If your system does not, you'll have to settle for tick mark sheets. Give each agent a sheet of paper with all the call types and space to keep a running hash-mark count. Separately, you should determine the average talk time for each call type.

Step Four: analyze the charts prepared in Step Two. The central issues in reducing cost per transaction are as follows:
- Improve the ratio of agent on-phone vs. paid time
- Improve the performance of struggling agents
- Reduce the time it takes to handle calls (but not at the expense of quality)
- Reduce the number of calls handled

The first action is to examine the agent sign-on charts looking for obvious indications that too much agent time shrinkage is taking place. Nothing hurts the cost per transaction more than paying for labor that is not applied to handling calls. Don't go overboard here, though. Becoming "time police" might temporarily lower cost per transaction, but in the long run creates other serious problems between the agents and management.

There are many legitimate off-phone activities in a contact center. Never forget that training is an investment in future performance improvements. Resist the urge to cancel training time and update sessions. Nevertheless, if it appears that you are losing too much agent time, there is no quicker way to impact cost per transaction than to take steps to recover the agent time shrinkage. If you have not implemented the charts in Chapter 6 already, you can use them and the data portrayed in one-on-one counseling discussions.

If the sign-on charts look good, take a quick look at the amount of outbound calling going on in the center. Even so-called pure inbound contact centers seem to generate some outbound calls. Sometimes the outbound calls are external to the firm, other times agents are calling various departments inside the company. In most cases, the inbound call generates the outbound call requirement. Calculate the ratio of outbound calls to inbound calls for the agent group and for individual agents. It is not unusual to find a large, significant difference in this ratio among agents. A high outbound to inbound call ratio often suggests an agent who is unsure about what department to call and whom to speak with to resolve questions and issues. If you see high ratios you might want to consider meeting with some of the agents who have low ratios to learn their secrets. Often, superstar agents develop their own tools. One of the more frequently created tools is the private telephone contact list. By collecting all the private contact lists and standardizing the information, every agent can quickly become more productive and efficient.

The next action would be to identify agents who are struggling with their jobs as evidenced by the normalized agent productivity charts. It is easy to use the agent transaction time chart to gain a cursory notion as to why the agent is struggling. Focus first upon agents with long wrap-up times before working with agents who have long talk times. It is likely that the agents with long wrap-up times have problems that can be resolved more quickly than those with long talk times. Frequently, agents with long wrap-up times are having trouble with navigating the computer screens. A little focused training can produce some big results.

Identification and quick resolution of a few problems is important so that you can begin to demonstrate to the agent force and the operations team that improvements are possible. Once everyone is convinced that improving the status quo is both possible and achievable without grievous pain, more and better ideas will begin to emerge.

Step Five: Use Erlang statistics to determine the correct staffing levels for every 30-minute period of your business day. If you have to actually use paper Erlang tables, this task will take a lot of time. You will go straight to heaven upon your death, however. It would probably be better to find or acquire a software tool that performs Erlang calculations. There are several vendors in this industry. Some have free Erlang calculators available for download from their Web sites.

Most of these tools require the user to key in the average talk time, the average after-call work time, the service level target expressed as a percent of calls to be answered within "x" seconds and the number of calls expected in a half-hour. A good Erlang model produces extremely useful information including:
- Agents Required on the Phones
- Callers Not Getting Immediate Answer

- Callers Getting Immediate Answer
- Average Speed of Answer—All Calls
- Average Delay of Delayed Calls
- Callers Waiting Longer than X Seconds
  (Where X is 5, 10, 15, 20 and so on)
- Agent Occupancy
- Trunk Traffic To Be Carried (Hourly)

Examine your ACD traffic report to identify the number of calls entering the contact center during every 30-minute period of the work week. Use a spreadsheet so that you can create some simple graphs. In one column, place the time of day. In the next, put the number of call arrivals. Then, put in the number of agents as calculated by the Erlang tables. Finally, put in the number of agents you really had on the phones. Some systems report this as average agents signed-on. Aggregate sign-on time for each 30-minute period is preferred since this number is more precise about exactly how much agent labor actually is applied to the phones.

This exercise ensures that the agent labor you are already paying for is properly deployed through the day and the week. Once you have this data in graphical form, it may be easier to spot times of the day or week where the center is overstaffed. It may even be possible to recognize ways to move labor from surplus periods to understaffed periods. Either outcome is positive. Excess labor drives up cost per transaction. And, understaffing drives up cost per transaction as callers wait on your In-Wats "nickel." An additional problem caused by understaffing is that the call abandon rate will go up. As fewer calls are handled (because of abandons), the cost per transaction explodes upward.

Missing the recommended staffing number by just a little can have dramatically bad results as was underscored in Chapter 5.

Step Six: Continue to improve agent productivity by identifying struggling agents and working with them to improve their skills.

Step Seven: After you have at least one week's worth of good call transaction type data, there are several approaches to consider. One approach is to identify the transaction type that takes the longest average talk time. Provide some spot training for the agents regarding that transaction. If some tools would help, create them. This is an excellent task for the operations team.

A second approach requires more time and some spending authority. If the contact center does not have an IVR system, the transaction-type data will help you determine if IVR can make a positive impact in your operation. If there are a goodly number of calls coming in for information that agents fetch through a simple computer retrieval and read off the screen, you have an excellent opportunity. You can identify for management and yourself how much it costs to answer certain transactions with human agents compared to the cost of answering with an IVR system. Substituting IVR answers for human agent answers will almost always be more economical. A point of caution is in order: As you remove short, easy calls from the human agents, the contact center dynamics will change. The average talk time will rise. All else being the same, the cost per transaction for the human agent answered calls will rise. Don't let this alarm anyone. Always calculate the cost per transaction for all calls, including those answered by IVR to keep overall comparisons intact over time.

Beyond this point, attacking cost per transaction requires successive iterations of the above-mentioned thrusts. Keep in mind that maintaining a flat cost per transaction over time is a victory. All costs tend to rise. It's called the basic inflation rate. If you can keep your costs from rising, it is a victory as sweet as any other.

Outbound Calling Campaigns

Many centers operate in a blended mode where inbound calling is mixed with outbound telemarketing. Although telemarketing has a generally negative perception among consumers, outbound calling can play a key, essential role in customer relationship management. Calling your customers proactively to inform them about new products or services, or to simply thank them for their ongoing business is a great idea.

Happily, most centers segregate outbound telemarketing from inbound calling. While some agents move gracefully between these tasks, it is rare that inbound call handling and outbound call placement occurs in a mixed mode. Generally, agents are either handling inbound calls or they are attached to outbound telemarketing campaigns for discrete periods of time. This makes it fairly simple to calculate the cost of outbound tele-marketing campaigns. Simply segregate the time spent on telemarketing from inbound call handling. If you have dedicated, separate groups this is really easy. If you have blended agent teams, the easiest way is to simply use a percentage allocation scheme among inbound call handling and outbound campaigns. The process is the same.

Multimedia Transactions

Without belaboring the point, the process for calculating multimedia cost per transaction is largely the same as for inbound call handling. For the most part, contact centers that have implemented e-mail handling and Web site support are performing these tasks with dedicated agents making it very simple to calculate the cost per transaction. If your center is among the few that has mastered transaction blending via a universal queue, producing cost-per-transaction metrics will be more complicated, but not impossible. If your contact center technology is well integrated, you should be able to discern how much time is being spent on each kind of transaction. If not, you can work it out.

Chapter 8:
Observations, Opinions
and Speculations

Opinions are like personalities, everyone has one although some are more interesting than others. If you have been reading carefully, you may have already noticed that I have some opinions about selected subjects connected with contact centers. I placed a few of those opinions alongside discussions of technology or management practice where they seemed to make the most sense. But I have some opinions and observations that simply didn't fit elsewhere or are too speculative. You don't have to agree with me and many don't. The ultimate resolutions for these issues will emerge from the marketplace at large. Like Dennis Miller says after one of his now-famous rants, "I could be wrong."

Universal Queues Need Universal Agents

As more and more contact centers evolve from their voice-only roots, the vendor hypemeisters have found a new drum to beat with the notion of a universal queue. A universal queue is one in which all forms of customer contact are treated as a single stream of transaction requests, albeit with different importance to the firm and different response expectations on the part of the customer. The major benefit to the contact center management team is that operating with a universal queue almost guarantees a more cost-effective operation. Here's why.

You know that there are natural inefficiencies in a voice-only application. This was discussed in an earlier chapter. The random nature of call arrivals coupled with a desire to answer the caller within a fixed number of seconds implies that agents' occupancy will be less than 100%. In fact, we have learned that higher agent occupancy is always associated with poor service levels. This was identified as one of the unfortunate laws of call center operations. It was suggested that nobody could have higher agent occupancy and good service levels simultaneously.

But the inclusion of deferrable work can change that dynamic. E-mail message handling and Web site call-back requests are new transactions in the contact center that may permit us to achieve higher occupancy rates without negatively impacting service levels. The concept is really quite simple. When the contact center routing engine notices that the incoming call load is being successfully handled, e-mail transactions can be routed to agents who would otherwise remain in the available state. Conditional routing elements can be constructed to help ensure that all the available agents are not given e-mail transactions, since that would be inimical to dealing with random arrivals of voice callers.

There is just one problem with universal queues, they require universal agents. Frankly, I think it is difficult enough to be an agent today without the additional stress of not knowing what kind of transaction will pop up next. The technology is not the issue here.

The ability for an agent to shift from application to application and from medium to medium seems asking for too much. We already encounter many agents who insist that they not be included in call blending operations where inbound and outbound calling are mixed. And this argument has been going on for more than 15 years! Customer service agents, skilled in dealing with incoming callers, swear that they cannot deal with outbound calls. Keep in mind that the difference between these two kinds of calls can frequently be described as attitudinal rather than structural. That is, the mechanics of the call are nearly the same. What is different is the attitude of the agent and the demeanor of the caller.

Now contact center management teams contemplate asking agents to shift effortlessly not only between different transactions (tough enough) but between communication modalities. This is also being described as being part of a much-needed career path for agents. Industry analysts like GartnerGroup have envisioned a hierarchical agent workforce population as depicted below:

Figure 8-1. Agent Population Pyramid

At the base of the agent population pyramid are the entry-level agents, fresh out of basic training. They are capable of handling a particular class of transaction. Generally they are routine, uncomplicated interactions. Next up the skills ladder we find traditional, experienced agents. These agents have achieved a level of expertise through experience and training that enable them to handle any kind of voice telephone transaction that can be reasonably expected to enter the contact center. In most call centers, this is where the agent hierarchy ends. In 21st century contact centers, the agent skill pyramid has new levels.

Because contact centers will be handling e-mail and Web site support transactions, a new class of agent will quickly emerge. Gartner refers to them as "communication-surfers." This term highlights the central characteristic, shifting between communication modes as needed. During a work shift, agents in the communication-surfer role will handle voice telephone calls, e-mail messages and Web site support requests, as necessary. However, they will only deal with one communication mode at a time. That is to say, as a communication-surfer I would handle telephone calls for the first few hours and then shift into an e-mail handling group for several hours, as an example. Finally, at the top of the pyramid are the universal agents. These agents can handle any transaction in any mode at any time. Universal agents can never be sure exactly what transaction they will be presented with in the next moment or even what communication method will be employed.

GartnerGroup argues that it is probably unwise, and maybe impossible, to set a goal of having an entire population of universal agents. Such a center would be attractive in many different ways. 100% universal agents would position the center for the lowest possible labor time expenditure. Customer satisfaction would likely rise since no matter how a customer wanted to interact, the center would be ready. Indeed, possessing all universal agents solves nagging staffing problems associated with skill routing. Even with simulation tools, contact centers can face unexpected surges in demand. Having an entire center of totally flexible agents permits graceful handling of these typical, daily operational problems.

Contact center management teams should realize that a hierarchy of agents, like that depicted above, is desirable and natural. The percentages of each tier may vary by the nature of the contact center and the transactions being conducted. Smaller centers might want to consolidate the universal agent and communication-surfer categories together. A useful guideline for agent population tiers might be:

Universal agent	10%
Communication-surfer	15%
Experienced agent	50%
Entry level	25%

There are two keys to maintaining a healthy population mix. One key is training. Training is expensive and it is difficult to find the time necessary to perform that task. The other key is retention. It is difficult to keep agents in the contact center. Good agents can move to other companies or they can move on to other positions within the company. Both situations are bad for the contact center. Organizations are sometime reluctant to engage in skill-development training for agents because they are mobile.

Clearly, as an agent moves up the pyramid by gaining valuable skills, we can expect wage demands to rise in step. Because labor forms such a large percentage of contact center operating costs, organizations are very concerned with rising wage rates and take steps to reduce labor costs at every opportunity. This illustrates several paradoxical problems that plague all contact centers:

- Contact center agents are highly skilled professionals whose interactions with prospects and customers define the success or failure of more and more firms. And, we pay them and treat them exactly like clerks.
- As agent skill requirements in the contact center grow, contact center training budgets will need to increase. But, management teams will be reluctant to pay for skills-training programs if agents take advantage of the training and change jobs over wage differentials among centers.

In a sense, these two issues are related. It's one of the dirty little secrets of the contact center industry. We want our agents to provide great service, up-sell, cross-sell, instill customer loyalty, and create and foster relationships with our customers. And, we want them to do it for as little as possible. We want our agents to be highly skilled in a wide range of abilities. And, we would rather not provide the training, thank you.

There really has to be a way out of the apparent dilemma. Agents are going to require a lot of training in multimedia transactions and firms have a right to expect a reasonable return on their investments. The solution might be to draft employment agreements for contact center professional agents.

An employment agreement spells out the duties and responsibilities for all parties. Such an agreement might promise the agent a specified amount of classroom, computer-based training and other forms of training during the term of employment. The agent agrees to remain in the contact center for the specified period of time. Obviously, provisions need to be made for circumstances beyond reasonable control.

Employment agreements might be just the vehicle to raise the perception of the contact center agents' value both inside and outside the firm. Contact center agents need to be recognized as the professionals they are.

Wireless

The largest deposit of copper in the world used to be in Chile. Now it lies underneath the isle of Manhattan. It is the legacy of the last 125 years that a great deal of effort and money went into moving that copper from Chile to Manhattan. Along the way, the copper ore was transformed into copper telephone wires.

There are wires everywhere. Too many wires for our own good. It's no wonder that emerging nations in Asia and Africa don't have the slightest interest in duplicating our costly infrastructure in landline telephony. The emerging nations of the world are starting out wireless. And in an echo effect, the industrialized countries of the world are becoming increasingly infatuated with wireless technology.

There are roughly 200 million Internet users globally as of the end of 1999. And the growth rate for Internet users is quite high. Nonetheless, it doesn't match the penetration rate and growth rate of global wireless technology. At the end of 1999, it was estimated that there were 400 million mobile phone users in the world. This figure was expected to grow to more than a billion users by 2003. A billion users causes most business people to catch their breath. What a market!

William Safire, former speechwriter for President Nixon and a highly respected journalist with an affinity for the art and structure of language, recently coined a new term: M-Commerce. While much attention is being paid to e-commerce these days, Safire suggests m-commerce (for mobile commerce) might be more significant. M-commerce is really not new. It is a natural outcome of the ongoing convergence of voice and data. The difference is this: While e-commerce provides access to anyone at any time, m-commerce provides the next dimension—access to anyone from anywhere. The notion is that the Internet should not be limited to users of fixed desktop technologies but also from highways, while walking down the street and generally running around.

There are two terms that we will hear much more about in the near future: Wireless Application Protocol (WAP) and Bluetooth. Each, in it's own way, will remove wires from our lives.

The WAP standard was created by the WAP Forum (**www.wapforum.org**), a consortium of companies that includes the likes of Ericsson, Motorola, Nokia, IBM, Intel, Microsoft and Hewlett-Packard. The standards they are creating permit Internet Web site content to be displayed upon the small screen typically found in mobile phones. Typically, a server running enabling software bridges the gap between the Internet Web site and the mobile phone running a WAP browser. This server performs the necessary protocol and format conversions needed to transmit content to a mobile device. It turns out that this is not a trivial task. The reason is that Web pages today are created using Hypertext Markup Language (HTML). HTML is a language used to create the look of a Web page. It is like paint on a canvas. But like paint, HTML doesn't know anything about the stuff on the page. But WAP devices rely upon programming and display languages called WMLscript and the Wireless Markup Language (WML), which is an Extensible Markup Language (XML) derivative optimized for tiny displays. It is important to realize that WML pages are typically less than 50 characters long. HTML Web pages aren't simply reduced to fit onto wireless devices, they are usually completely re-engineered.

XML is a way to stick little software-coded labels on stuff. The technical people refer to this as "metadata" which is a fancy term that means data about the data. If I can tag every piece of interesting data with information about the nature and structure of that data, I don't have to worry as much about writing interfaces between devices. If every Web page were written in XML instead of HTML, it would be like having a common language and currency for the entire planet. Everything digital could work together to make life easier.

Tiny displays are just one issue. The other issue has to do with data transmission speeds. Today, wireless data rates top out at about 14.4 KBPS. All of the major wireless carriers have projects under way that are designed to improve the reach of wireless data communications, as well as the speed. Over the next few years, we should see wireless data rates routinely at 384 KBPS and perhaps as high as 2 MBPS. Even so, tiny screens and slower data rates preclude flashy graphic displays or visually engaging interactions.

WAP technology is exciting and interesting because of the vast number of mobile phone users in the world. WAP applications are more prevalent in Europe than anywhere else for two good reasons. First, mobile phone users in the United States are plagued by three incompatible carrier network technologies: CDMA (code division multiple access), TDMA (time division multiple access) and GSM (global system for mobile communications). Second, mobile phone users in the United States are charged on a per-minute price basis, resulting in a significant consumer cost in using a mobile phone to browse the Web. In contrast, European mobile phone users have just one network technology, GSM, and most pricing models are based on a flat-fee structure.

How will WAP technology intersect the contact center? Simple. It will be another path to self-service and another avenue within which to create customer loyalty. In addition to benefits associated with accessing information on the move, WAP technology conveys another important piece of information about the customer: their location. Knowing where the customer physically is opens an entirely new range of "push" services. For example, the travel industry is already experimenting with WAP applications. Soon, it will not be farfetched to ask your mobile phone for lunch recommendations based on your current location. Or suppose you finish a business meeting in a distant city earlier than expected. Hopping into a taxi, the businessperson can dial in on their mobile phone, bring up their current reservation, go back to see earlier flights, and hit enter to rebook a ticket. Pushing technology convergence even further, WAP-enabled mobile phones can be augmented by natural language, speaker independent, voice recognition so as to understand full sentences. This would permit a customer to say, "I need to go from Dallas to Chicago Monday morning." and have that converted into a screen display with the available flights.

Knowing the location of a mobile phone user opens up the opportunity to increase loyalty by offering the traveler services of interest such as nearby restaurants, driving directions, route optimization, news and financial information. In short, everything that is useful about the Web that we have learned how to use from fixed desktops is even more compelling and desirable when we are on the move. In the 21st century, we all seem to be on the move as never before. Mark Plakias of the Kelsey Group, a consulting and research group, predicts that voice access to the Internet will outstrip PC use by 2005. That would create some very interesting applications for contact centers as they naturally continue to provide support for Web visitors.

The other technology aimed at removing the wires from our lives is called Bluetooth. Bluetooth is an enabling technology that allows wireless communications between mobile phones and other devices, among different wireless devices, between mobile phones and Bluetooth-enabled appliances and among appliances. Simply, Bluetooth technology is a short-range radio on a single chip (amazingly small, 1 centimeter square) that can translate digital data from computers. The radio sends and receives voice and data signals that come within the broadcast range of 30 feet (already there is some talk of extending the range to 300 feet). Because radio waves pass through walls and other barriers, Bluetooth devices can communicate in situations that stop rival technologies, like infrared. This technology probably won't have a major impact on contact centers, per se. One likely improvement based on Bluetooth technology is the wireless headset. Agents can become untethered. But based on the notion of convenience, Bluetooth may have a major impact on our lives. A Bluetooth-enabled mobile phone becomes a cordless extension phone the moment you enter your home. It functions like a walkie-talkie when communicating with another Bluetooth mobile phone within its broadcast range. It could also unlock your automobile and set the radio to your favorite station as you walk up to the parking lot. The applications become even more interesting as one contemplates having a WAP mobile phone with Bluetooth embedded. Armed with such a device, a business traveler could cruise through life, broadcasting basic, pertinent information about themselves to intelligent devices imbedded in such things as electronic door locks, car rental buses and hotel check-in counters. Think of it as "screen popping" your way through life.

Customer Relationship Management

By now, we are all aware that CRM is a strategy rather than a product. If you ask five people to define it, you are likely to get five different answers. But that's because CRM is a lot like water, it takes the shape of its container. Unlike water, it is comprised of many components. Let's define CRM as being principally about retaining existing customers, acquiring new customers and getting more revenue from them. At the beginning of the 21st century, the accepted wisdom is that such a strategy is realized when the enterprise provides:

- Multiple points of contact
- Different methods of communication
- Self-service options
- Assisted-service options
- Cross-department and cross-function data sharing
- Rich customer database
- Efficient workflow
- Well-defined processes

You'll have to agree, it's a pretty daunting list of attributes. *Information Week*, a magazine aimed at business technology issues, polled nearly 500 U.S.-based companies. They were surprised to discover that one-half had not even *begun* to evaluate CRM solution providers. The single biggest reason given: cost. Full-blown CRM initiatives can cost millions of dollars and take several years. It doesn't really have to be this way.

CRM Lite

In a real sense, call centers have been engaged in customer relationship management for years. Yes, when call centers add multimedia transactions we find it necessary to change their name to contact center. And, yes this is a major transition with significant technology and training issues. But that doesn't alter the fact that call centers have been focused upon customers for a long time. By recognizing that core competency within many, many companies today, is to begin to implement the highest payback areas promised by CRM solutions.

A shorthand way of thinking about CRM is simply "treating different customers differently." This is where to start. Does your company segment its customers? Do you know who are your best customers? Do you have some customers that you really should not have because they cost you more than you'll ever realize in return? These are the fundamental questions that you need to ask before embarking on a CRM initiative.

While it might be really powerful to engage in one-to-one marketing, wherein each customer is treated in a unique manner consistent with their preferences and their value to your firm, it might be enough to segment your customers into three groups. We don't need fancy identifiers for these groups, let's simply refer to them as Tier A, Tier B and Tier C customers. Tier A customers are your best customers. Each company will have to decide what criteria to establish to populate the segments. Some firms will key on revenues. Others will key on profit. Some companies will decide that certain customers are "strategic," regardless of the revenue and profit associated with them. Tier B customers will likely comprise the largest group. These are your good customers. With work, some of them will move into the top tier. With proper handling, most will remain in Tier B. Some, hopefully few, will find their way into Tier C, which are customers that are not generating much revenue or profit and might be negatively affecting your bottom line.

Make no mistake. Sorting your customers into just these three segments will require lots of work and take a lot of time, but it is worth the effort. Once you have the three tiers defined and sorted, begin a structured program to learn how members of each tier want to be treated. Obviously, it makes sense to focus on the Tier A customers first. Since they are providing significant revenues and profits, you should strive to find ways to bind these customers more closely to your company. Give them special access into the contact center via a special number or hidden auto-attendant menu choice. Connect them with your best agents. Learn their communication preferences. While the trade press suggests that everyone wants and needs Web access and e-mail interactions, it might be prudent to ask each of your best customers exactly how they would like to interact with you. Don't overlook easy, yet effective, tactics. How about establishing an outbound call list that represents your best customers? When inbound call volume slacks off, as it usually does at some point in the day, why not call your Tier A customers? You don't have to try to sell them anything. You could simply thank them for being your customer and ask them if there is something you can do for them today.

Go one step further. Try to discover why they are your best customers. See if you can create a generalized model of your best customer. To accomplish this, you will discover that there are two kinds of data required—internal and external data. Examples of internal data include account balance, transaction data, promotion history, customer service requests, revenue received and, possibly, the profitability of that customer. Most companies have this kind of information. Unfortunately, it is seldom found in one database and that is a real problem. However, to construct meaningful "best customer" models you will need external data, as well.

Examples of external data include demographics, socioeconomic information, geography, and so forth. Most companies do not possess this kind of information about their customers. Yet, it is essential in constructing the "best customer" model. The development of this model is key to the most important element of CRM—transforming Tier B customers into Tier A customers.

Every company has experienced the frustration associated with having two customers with similar profiles but very different revenue histories. The central question is why? By understanding as much as possible about your Tier A customers, you can target a subset of Tier B customers with a higher probability of transforming them into Tier A customers.

Which brings us to the Tier B and C customers. If we can't transform B's into A's, then at minimum we should strive to keep them as Tier B's. Contact centers have experience at the status quo game. You should try to understand Tier B's communication preferences. Maintenance of good service levels coupled with quick resolution of issues will go a long way towards retaining B customers. Contact center agents should be equipped and encouraged to help both B and C level customers learn how to use available self-servicing tools on your Web site and through your IVR systems. A great way to accomplish this is the guided tour and it is particularly effective for IVR systems. The agent, realizing they are connected to a B or C level customer, completes the transaction. But before releasing the customer, asks if they are aware of and have taken advantage of the self-service option. After receiving permission from the caller, the agent establishes a three-way conference call that joins the caller, agent and IVR into a single connection. The agent "walks" the caller through the IVR script and demonstrates how the caller could have obtained the same information without speaking with an agent.

With respect to Tier C customers, sales and marketing executives should assess whether the firm would be better off without these customers. Clearly, if our best customer profiling has been effective, you will find C customers that have the potential to move up in the rankings. And, programs should be created and executed to achieve that goal. But there are Tier C customers that will forever remain in that category. If you believe that they contribute to the bottom line, then the goal should be to reduce the cost of servicing them as much as possible. Efforts should be made to direct Tier C customers to self-help processes.

CRM doesn't have to mean spending millions of dollars on software. Many of the benefits associated with this strategy can be achieved with lesser expenditures. Transforming a call center into a contact center does not have to cost a fortune. Providing the requisite training to your agents in order to enable them to utilize multimedia communication modes will require time and money. Both are usually scarce resources.

Is There a Dark Side to CRM?

Eastern cultures see the world through a slightly different lens. One of the manifestations of this tendency is the concept of yin and yang. Most people have encountered the pictogram that represents this concept. It is a circle surrounding two symmetric shapes, one white and one black. It is emblematic of the dual nature inherent in so many things. We can be alternately pleasant and ugly. Times can be good and then bad. Everything ultimately is seen to possess harmony and balance.

When it comes to the hype surrounding CRM, the concept of yin and yang doesn't seem pertinent. CRM appears to offer only positive benefits. Vendors and the trade press suggest that only good things flow from CRM initiatives. OK, maybe the only semi-bad thing associated with CRM is that it might be expensive. And, many CRM initiatives undertaken up to this point have not returned the investment. But having admitted those flaws, the conventional wisdom suggests that companies belly up to the payment bar or risk becoming roadkill on the information superhighway.

I think that there may be at least three areas that haven't received much attention in the CRM frenzy: privacy, relevancy and causality. Just a few pages ago we touched upon a key factor for success implicit in a CRM initiative—data. Peppers and Rodgers aside, it is probably not likely that many firms will succeed in the pursuit of one-to-one marketing. If you have a million customers then one-to-one marketing implies a million marketing messages, a million Web pages and a million promotions. As a result, customer modeling and segmentation are more practical approaches. And, it seems clear that internal data won't be enough to construct meaningful models. You will need external data—demographics—to flesh out the models and make them actionable.

And there lies the rub. My sense is that people around the world are growing more concerned about the amount of personal information being collected and sometimes shared among organizations. I realize that sometimes when companies have an enhanced view of us as consumers, they are in a position to proactively delight us with suggestions and recommended courses of action. But I believe that more and more people are simply not interested in having lots of personal data floating around cyberspace. I don't think that this is a recent shift in attitude either. There is an apocryphal story that I have heard many times concerning the first screen-pop application ever implemented. American Express, many years ago, spent a small fortune implementing one of the very first screen-pop routines where automatic number identification is used to populate the agent's screen with the caller's data. On the fateful day when the application was first cut over into service, many executives were gathered in the call center to witness the occasion. As the first call was processed, the lucky agent greeted the caller by name instead of reciting the standard greeting and asking for the card number. The caller's response was to hang up. The executives were slightly ruffled and some sidelong glances were cast. The second call entered the system. The receiving agent greeted that caller by name and was promptly dragged into a 5-minute conversation on how the agent was able to greet the caller by name. Given that the central justification for the significant dollars invested was to reduce talk time and produce greater satisfaction, the executives were nonplussed with a hang-up on the first call and a lengthy diatribe on the second.

The moral of that story, if there is one, might be that people don't always want or need tight relationships with businesses. They demand good service but not at the expense of their privacy or even their perceived sense of privacy. Frequently, I hear authorities in the industry talk about how CRM can permit firms to be proactive with their customers. A frequent example proffered has a bank customer calling in about some minor customer service issue. After resolving the minor matter, the CRM-enabled agent launches into a discussion of mutual funds available from the bank because the caller's profile and account status suggests that they might be receptive to that pitch. I think it is just as likely that the caller is going to be slightly taken aback at the agent's intrusion into their financial details as it is that the caller will be delighted with the suggestion.

The next point to consider in thinking about CRM is relevancy. While all firms have customers, not all customers require a relationship with the companies they choose to do business with. In fact, I believe that people, in general, require very few relationships with companies they do business with. Do you need a relationship with a bookstore, grocery store, retail clothier, appliance store, record store or trash hauler? Probably not. Which companies do you need a deep relationship with? If you are like me, the list is not very long. All I need are decent products and services delivered on time and billed correctly. If something goes awry, I would prefer it if the firm is easy to contact and that I can get my problem resolved with a minimum of time and effort. So, the very idea that all companies should initiate CRM projects seems to be overreaching.

The last point I want to make has to do with causality. Vendors and the trade press have greatly oversimplified the situation. To hear them tell it, CRM initiatives are the difference between survival and corporate death. Maybe so. In a survey performed by *InformationWeek* involving 175 information technology professionals whose companies have implemented CRM-enabling technologies, customer satisfaction has been measured and tracked before and after the CRM project. Unhappily, just 35% of the respondents reported significant improvement in customer satisfaction; 46% of the respondents indicated only slight improvement in the satisfaction measures; and 15% reported absolutely no difference whatsoever. The article did not indicate what the remaining 4% reported.

If I sound negative about CRM, it's not intentional. I think market segmentation is smart and necessary, but I don't think firms need to spend millions of dollars on new software suites to achieve the benefits that CRM purportedly provides. I think what we are dealing with is a phenomenon associated with all technologies that GartnerGroup has dubbed the "Trough of Disillusionment." Gartner suggests that nearly all technologies elicit high praise and exciting speculation about its impact upon the enterprise when the first PowerPoint slides appear. The fever grows as the number of vendors and the trade press begins to churn the subject. Early adopters of the technology begin implementations. Results sometimes diverge from expectation. As more real-world implementations are attempted, valuable experience is gained regarding the true boundaries and limitations of the technology. This produces the disillusionment trough. After that, the hype subsides somewhat and the real impact (or lack thereof) of that technology begins to emerge from actual experiences on a broad scale. The chart depicting all this follows:

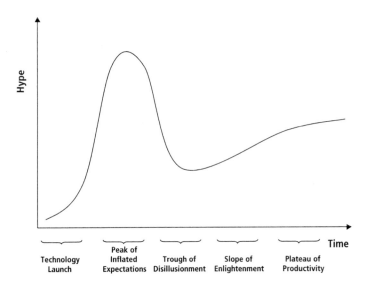

Figure 8-2. Technology Hype Life Cycle

The curve feels right to me although I think there are differences in its shape, wavelength and amplitude among different technologies. The point is that full-blown CRM initiatives are risky and can potentially cost millions. Ultimately it's not a decision involving "if" but rather one involving "when." This doesn't mean firms can choose to ignore the fundamental points of a CRM strategy or enhanced contact center customer touch-points today.

Contact Center Size and Multilocation Architecture

There are some common, recurring questions in every industry that never seem to get fully resolved. Instead they ebb and flow between two poles. Contact center agent size and the related issue of how to architect multilocation centers seems to be one of those questions. Let's take a look.

How big should my center be? I could suggest that this question isn't relevant anymore. Technically, I can utilize 100% remote agents and my physical center is rather small, no matter how big the contact volume grows. Admittedly, few organizations are willing or able to move towards 100% remote agents. Most will prefer a more formal office environment for a variety of reasons. As the number of agents working under one roof in a contact center grows, outside of physical constraints, there probably is some point beyond which the increasing population starts to become less cohesive and less productive. Often, there are physical constraints that demand the creation of a second location (and even a third) before the first center grows dysfunctionally large. Nevertheless, it seems reasonable to argue that at some size a contact center becomes more difficult to manage successfully.

It is already clear that as the agent population expands, the center becomes more expensive to operate. At minimum, the center will see higher and higher marginal agent recruitment and training costs as their required headcount expands. There are only so many people able and willing to be contact center agents in one area; some areas of the world are already saturated with respect to contact centers.

Conversations with users operating so-called megacenters bear striking similarities. If they could do it over again, they wouldn't. The dominant airline companies in the United States all operate a network of centers. Some of those centers are individually huge, housing between 1,000 and 1,500 agents. They look and feel like small cities. Acquiring space for all the cars is daunting. They are in the food business via company cafeterias. They are in the childcare business by virtue of the day care centers necessary to ensure agents keep their schedules. In an effort to make these megacenters livable, platoons of people organize book fairs, wellness campaigns, charity events, and so on. And the megacenters are expensive to keep staffed.

In my opinion, the perfect size for a contact center under one roof is somewhere between 80 and 150 agent positions. These boundaries are arbitrary, I know. At the upper end, the center would have 10 supervisors managing teams of 15 agents each. With attrition averaging about 25% per year, there would be almost one new person entering the center each week. My feeling is that with populations greater than 150, a disabling anonymity sets in as agents lose the sense of team and the sense that their individual effort makes some difference.

As your center grows or as other issues dictate more and more, organizations find themselves contemplating a second, third or fourth center. Apart from the question about where the centers should be located is the question regarding the technology approach.

It is fair to say that up to this point, most organizations have opted for a second, third or fourth physical center. This implies another set of technology tools in the form of ACD, IVR, CTI, and local area network. It also implies another set of center support and management staff. It further implies some approach to dividing the work among the multiple centers. The justification for this approach lies in disaster planning. Even in the event of a total calamity, you can reasonably expect that your other centers will be unaffected and able to conduct business as usual. And, it is an easy decision to make. Literally, one can use the first center as a template for successive, cookie-cutter installations in other venues.

I believe that in the future we will see a new approach become much more popular: the bunkered single system. This was discussed in the section on virtual systems. As carriers lay more optical fiber in pipelines and along railroads, the transmission cost structure is rapidly changing. I am suggesting that it soon will be less expensive to place a single large system in a secure building with uninterruptible power supplies, physical and environmental controls than it will be to establish and operate multiple centers made virtual by network routing. Instead, the bunkered single-system approach relies upon reliable, inexpensive flat rate T-1 lines as opposed to variable cost network routing. Open a second, third or fourth site and provision it with remote shelves instead of a complete new system. It is already a requirement that other sites have high-speed data connections to the rest of the enterprise. Since voice and data are converging, I expect that the remote shelf concept will gain in popularity.

The economic key to this approach is a low-cost, virtual private network. If Sprint and Worldcom believe that they can charge the U.S. government agencies less than a penny a minute for long distance in a few years and still make money, I believe that signals an oversupply of bandwidth of epic proportions. It should be possible to negotiate very favorable rates for virtual private networks. These VPNs will carry data and voice in the form of packets, and we don't have to worry about packet delay, latency or jitter because the packets never enter the so-called wild, wooly public Internet.

The Persistence of E-Mail

E-mail is growing quickly as an alternative form of communication. Prompted by Web site visits, e-mail is often more convenient than placing a free phone call. Vendors and trade press often discuss e-mail as simply another form of communication that has much in common with telephone calls and some important differences. Frequently, the major difference between e-mail and phone calls is the fact that e-mail is deferrable work. While that is certainly true, I think there is a much more significant difference.

Phone calls are ephemeral. E-mail is permanent. Phone calls happen and then they are literally gone and can't be recaptured exactly. Legally, one cannot record a telephone conversation and use it in a legal proceeding. So, arguments that swirl around who said exactly what during a phone conversation devolve into a form of "he said" and "she said." But e-mail messages have a very different nature; they hang around and have legal status even if they aren't signed in the literal sense. In the federal government of the United States, e-mail archives have already been subpoenaed to discover who knew what, when. In the Microsoft antitrust case, internal e-mail memos were introduced into the court proceedings and were instrumental in the court's decision.

Some firms are very concerned about the ramifications of the legal status suffusing e-mail messages. I am aware of several companies that refuse to accept e-mail messages for this very reason. Other firms accept e-mail messages and permit them to be processed by trained agents. But before the "send" button is depressed, the e-mail replies are routed through the legal department for oversight and approval. In an effort to streamline this cumbersome process, some companies have legal counsel prepare boilerplate responses to frequently asked questions. Yet the point remains: E-mail messages are legal documents and companies must think hard about the implications.

What Kind of Employee is a Contact Center Agent?

Many years ago, a colleague predicted that there would come a day when computers were so powerful and software so sophisticated that you could use a minimum-wage-scale agent in a world-class contact center. As call centers transform into contact centers under the influence of the Internet and multimedia interactions, many experts suggest that the skill level requirements for agents will increase dramatically with a concomitant rise in wages. Which of these scenarios is the more likely? Can we augment modestly skilled agents with silicon intelligence?

This is not simply a rhetorical question. If you subscribe to the notion that employees will require more and diverse skills to function as world-class contact center agents, then you also must worry about recruitment and retention. If, on the other hand, you believe that computers and software will someday permit low-skill employees to perform at world-class levels, then you don't have to be concerned about recruitment and retention.

I suggest that this issue is not binary. The resolution depends upon what kind of center the enterprise really wants and needs. It seems to me that this industry is actually comprised of three very distinct subcultures. There are, in my opinion, call factories, professional centers and strategic customer relationship centers. There are technology, management process and people differences quite clearly evident among the three subcultures. Consider the following:

Operational development →	Process	Technology	People
Relationship Management Centers	Managed Processes with Continuous Improvement	Contact Center integral business element. Homogeneous Contact Center/IT Infrastructure	Long term people development and retention
Professional Centers	Operational, management and development processes in place	Strong MIS. IVR, CTI, Web integration	Better recruiting processes. On-going, remedial training
Call Factories	Simple operational Processes	ACD in place but not well integrated with IT	People recruited with basic training. Survive or perish

Figure 8-3. Contact Center Subcultures

The chart portion of interest here is the "people" column. If you operate a call factory it is likely that you recruit people with basic skills and provide a minimal amount of training. There is a likelihood that inbound and outbound scripting is used to flatten the learning curve. Retention of trained agents is considered a bonus. Turnover rates in excess of 50% are not uncommon. The center management focuses upon time management and short transaction times. Quality, if it is considered at all, is built into the script flows and is often indistinguishable from efficiency.

As a center moves up in operational development and also becomes more integrated with the business purpose, agents are regarded in a slightly different light. Well-developed human resource practices are brought to bear on agent recruitment to minimize avoidable turnover. Telephone interviews are conducted with potential agents to gain insight into how they conduct themselves on the phone. Typically, more thorough training regimens are developed that combine classroom and on-the-phone exercises. Mentoring enters the picture. Individual agent metrics are calculated and used to identify people who seem to be struggling with the task so that remedial training and coaching resources can be intelligently applied. While efficiency still plays an important role in the philosophy of the center management, effectiveness becomes a new concern.

But things change dramatically in centers that are organized and empowered to promote customer relationships, build loyalty and improve top- and bottom-line performance of the enterprise. While the trade press waxes eloquent about the benefits of forging closer relationships with customers, it is strangely silent about forging closer ties with and creating greater loyalty among the center's agents. I find this unsettling. If one agrees that the lifetime value of a good customer is significant and worth investing in, then it seems evident that the same must be true for a good contact center agent.

That said, it becomes important to determine which kind of center you want and need versus the kind of center you currently possess. One way to determine this is to understand whether the center is an entry point into the company or whether it is a place that existing employees aspire to join.

Application Service Provisioning

There has been much "buzz" in the computer industry trade press lately about Application Service Providers (ASPs). What may not really be clear, despite the widespread coverage, is what they are and what they do. At a minimum, they host software applications for organizations. These applications can include e-commerce software, Enterprise Resource Planning packages, accounting packages, sales force automation packages, knowledge management and corporate communications packages. By combining software, hardware, networking technologies and technical expertise, ASPs provide superior performance and increased security, reliability and scalability over traditional corporate-owned, in-house, corporate-run applications—without a significant upfront financial commitment.

In a real sense, ASPs are a "back to the future" phenomenon. In the 1970s and early 1980s there were firms that provided "time-sharing" services. In the '70s and early '80s many firms could not afford to install and maintain certain mainframe applications, so they outsourced the hosting of these applications to third-party providers (then called time-sharing services). The fact that these applications were run on centrally hosted machines, like IBM Mainframes and Digital Equipment Corporation's minicomputer VAX, facilitated this trend.

The technology issues facing companies today are analogous to those of the past; expensive hardware, applications with a need for a high degree of customization, software that requires a relatively high degree of technical sophistication to maintain, and a shortage of qualified technicians to implement all of the above. Web-based applications, like their mainframe predecessors, are centrally hosted and maintained.

In an increasingly competitive world, small and medium-sized businesses need the information technology tools of larger firms, yet, in general, they lack the resources to build and maintain such an environment. Even divisions of large firms cannot always get the attention of the overtaxed IT departments, but they do have the budgetary independence to outsource applications.

ASPs can bridge the gap for these customers. They can provide information technology at a reasonable cost through their ability to specialize and rapidly deploy these centrally hosted applications. According to industry analysts, Application Service Provisioning is slated to become the dominant model for software application delivery. ASP customers can rent services on a per-user, per-month basis (or several other payment models) at a fraction of the cost of purchasing, deploying and supporting traditional high-end business applications.

ASP Business Models

Application Service Providers come in all shapes and sizes. The skill sets they bring to the table vary widely and most combine some or all of the following skills. Broadly they fall into the following categories:
1. Data Communications Specialists
2. Hosting Specialists
3. Application Development Specialists

Data Communications Specialists

Data Communications Specialists are experts at network uptime. The skill sets to do this vary, but include:
1. TCP/IP expertise—knowledge of DNS, firewalls, mail protocols, etc.... Their job is to ensure adequate response time to your applications from your location or anywhere on the Internet (particularly when involving e-commerce application).
2. Network configuration and monitoring—They have the ability to put into place a wide variety of network equipment (Ethernet cards, bridges, switches, routers) and ensure their correct configuration. Once the network has been put into place, ASPs need the expertise to install the software packages that will allow them to anticipate where difficulties are beginning to occur and to takes steps to ensure that the equipment is reconfigured and repaired. Ideally, the user should never sees these actions taking place.
3. Disaster Recovery—No matter how well prepared, there is the inevitable interference from the outside world: errant backhoe operators, fires in the data center. The question is not if these outside forces will cause problems, but when.

Hosting Specialists

Hosting Specialists fall into four broad categories (a single ASP may have overlap in multiple categories):

1. Hosting of Web pages—These providers allow organizations to host "static" Web pages on the servers at their location.
2. Co-location providers—These firms allow companies to host their servers in "cages" in the ASPs data center. Typically the maintenance of the machines (software; hardware, like Ethernet cards; hard drives, motherboards) is left to the customer. Most firms focused on co-location are not considered to be ASPs, since, in a very real sense, they are not "providing applications"; they are providing physical security and bandwidth.
3. E-commerce hosting—Historically these firms have taken "prepackaged" e-commerce applications, made slight variations, and hosted the applications. Recently, however, a new breed of ASP has been providing a much greater level of customization and integration with the customer's existing information technology systems.
4. Non-e-commerce applications—This is the newest area of services for ASPs. These firms provide hosting of Enterprise Resource Planning packages, accounting packages, sales force automation packages, knowledge management and corporate communications packages. These organizations might host custom applications built either internally, by the customer or by a third-party consulting firm.

In situations where the hosting firm is responsible for the platform on which the applications are hosted, they should be experts in that hardware/software platform and have great expertise in backup and recovery, in the event of a crash or other catastrophic disaster.

Application Development Specialists

These firms have project management and application development engineers on their staff. They are experts in building client-server based applications and, more importantly, Web-based applications from scratch or modifying commercial, off-the-shelf packages.

Their business models tend to fall into the following categories:

1. "No-cost" application development—Of course there are costs associated with developing these applications, but they are amortized over the life of the hosting contract. The most important issue to be negotiated here is who owns the resulting application code at the end of the contract, the ASP or the using organizations.
2. "Fixed Fee" development projects—These are projects in which the contracting organization clearly owns the resulting code but costs are front-loaded. Often there is a lengthy planning process and contractual requirement to adhere to the specification.

3. "Time and Materials" projects—The contracting organization clearly owns the code at the end of the project and the project costs are front-loaded. Planning should also be a part of the process, but the customer has the flexibility to change the requirements of the project to meet changing business requirements, even in the middle of the development process.

Application Service Provisioning and Telephony

An interesting question is whether a market opportunity exists by applying ASP business models to the provisioning of customer contact technologies. Customer contact technology, in its current state of the art, consists of hardware and software. In the existing ASP business models, hardware content is fundamentally restricted to industry-standard servers and routers. In the customer contact market, a significant portion of the hardware is semiproprietary. That, in itself, presents some issues.

In a real sense, customer contact and even basic voice communications are already available from multiple ASPs. We call these ASPs "Telephone Operating Companies" and the service offering is known as "Centrex." While Centrex services have enjoyed varying degrees of success in other nations (most notably Australia and the UK), Centrex has never achieved significant market share within the U.S. customer contact industry.

It is generally felt that the reasons why Centrex customer contact initiatives have not generated success include:
- Perceived loss of control by user
- Below par routing and reporting
- Difficulties associated with CTI implementation
- Cost of service offering

Given these impediments to Centrex in the United States it seems unlikely that complete customer contact systems will be offered within the ASP business model.

2010

Near-term speculations almost always are straight-line projections of the present. Longer-term speculations are less precise but a lot more fun. No, I don't foresee flying automobiles, individual rocket backpacks or direct Internet links into the human cortex, but there are some seemingly farfetched ideas that I believe will come about within 10 years that have a bearing on the way we will interact with firms.

Several technologies, already mentioned, play a key role in shaping the world of 2010. Speech recognition and wireless data communication will ultimately be robust enough to alter the straight-line paths we have been following. The other major factor shaping the year 2010 is that computers, as such, will disappear. They won't be replaced with something new, rather computers will be inside devices that appear familiar to us but operate in fundamentally different ways. For example, there may well be a device on the kitchen counter that resembles a radio in that it permits one to listen to radio stations. However, it is not a radio in the normal sense at all. It does not snag radio waves out of the air. Instead it delivers streaming audio from thousands of radio stations around the world via the Internet. Similarly, there is likely something akin to a television in the family room. It might even be hooked up to cable. But the signals it receives are streaming video from the Internet. And it doubles as a two-way, real-time communication device.

Today the computer reigns. Desktop computers have given way to laptops. Laptops continue to shrink. At some point, the reduction in computer size will stop if for no other reason than human fingers imply a certain size keyboard, even if manipulating a stylus. Things will change dramatically when speech recognition reaches its first maturity. The most obvious change will be the disappearance of the keyboard as an input device. Think *Star Trek*. I don't think I have ever seen a qwerty keyboard in a *Star Trek* episode. Instead, they speak to the computer in sentences. The related technology of text to speech endows the computer with a voice. This will solve a myriad of problems facing computer users today. For example, most people use perhaps 10% of the functionality of Microsoft Word. The main reason is that it is difficult to remember and navigate through the GUI point-and-click interface available today. The user must remember that certain functionality is under Format and is several layers deep in nested commands. Because the command is out of sight, it is often out of mind. Speech recognition will permit users to tell their computers what they want done instead of how to do something. If the computer doesn't understand, it will ask questions until it has removed any ambiguity from the request.

Once speech recognition reaches maturity, road warriors and knowledge workers can quit imitating Batman, who moved through all kinds of situations and adversities gracefully by virtue of the many contraptions hanging from his utility belt. It is not unusual to see a knowledge worker toting a laptop augmented by several plug-in devices and at least two different power cords, a mobile phone clipped to one side of the belt and a pager clipped to the other side. In the briefcase lies a personal digital assistant (PDA) that keeps tabs on appointments, phone numbers and "to do" lists. One wonders how much time is spent on simply synching all these devices periodically.

It is likely that a single, small device will replace all this paraphernalia. Think of this device as a mobile phone on steroids. For convenience let's refer to it as a hyperphone. Instead of attempting to use the telephone keypad as an input device, the hyperphone will respond to spoken commands articulated in natural language. Whereas today we have an ear-bud speaker/microphone input/output mechanism, in 2010 the hot accessory will include a headmounted display typically positioned over one eye so as not obscure everyday vision. Today very few people even take notice of someone apparently speaking out loud to themselves as they stroll through the airport concourse. In 2010 nobody will take notice of headmounted displays. For recreational purposes, a variation on the single-eye headmount will offer binocular headmounted displays where each image is slightly offset from the other, rendering a lovely 3-D effect.

As wireless data transmission rates soar, normal transactions conducted by simple phone will be augmented with visual displays. As consumers, we will be confronted with two different types of agents. Web sites will be provisioned with anthropomorphic agents that will transform self-service. An anthropomorphic agent is a construct. It could be a cartoon, a static image or more likely, a highly detailed depiction of a human face with recognizable expressions, moving lips synchronized with the words and eye movements. Think of anthropomorphic Web agents as IVR on steroids—with a face.

The second type of agent we will deal with will be a real person, although privacy issues will render them unrecognizable. Tier A customers will be permitted to have live interactions with human agents but, because video over IP (or its successor) will facilitate a view of each other, many human agents will demand the creation and use of an avatar. Similar to the anthro-pomorphic agent, an avatar is an embodiment of a person. It is an artificial depiction representing a person. Instead of transmitting the agent's face, the system will project an artificial image of the agent's choosing. In better implementations, the database containing important customer management information will also identify which, from among many avatars available, is the one that the customer prefers. It is also likely that an entire science will develop around the concept of avatars suited to particular transactions. For example, a customer complaint hotline might be staffed by avatar images that look like someone's grandmother. Confronted with a grandmotherly image, how many irate customers might be immediately calmed down to a more rational level?

So, It's Communication You Want?

Life is a wheel. It is circular. It is a journey. What came before, comes again, although sometimes slightly transformed in the process. History really does contain the answers to the questions posed by an unknown future. Humanity has longed for better and better communication and the death of distance for millennia. Why?

I submit that inside our skins, at the core, we are all lonely. Our nervous systems inform us about ourselves and the world within which we live in the most intimate ways and we perceive ourselves very directly. It all changes dramatically at the surface of our skins. We lose connectivity. Our nervous systems don't extend beyond our bodies. Yet.

Ultimately, the Internet involves functionality and speed that mimics our nervous systems so that we can intimately know each other and our shared environment in ways we can't begin to image today. We might never achieve the connectedness of the Vulcan mind-meld, but a good approximation might be found in an always-on, always-connected communication-based external nervous system. We've already moved from "What hath God wrought?" via electronic dots and dashes to "Mr. Watson, come here, I need you" via the amplification of sound waves through copper. Seen in another light, the history of man has been a continuous struggle to get outside our skins. The Internet is simply the next step in the ongoing quest. I don't know where it will all end. Perhaps in some future society, people will have TCP/IP connections planted directly into their cerebral cortex. Might we someday be greeted by a thought-gram reminding us that we are important to the company and please standby while our personal assistant comes online?

Index

Glossary

ACD Interflow—A system feature wherein a call waiting in queue for an answer resource is offered to other centers operated by the enterprise. In better implementations, the caller becomes queued at all sites waiting for the first appropriately skilled agent in any of the locations to become available.

Agent—A generic term applied to all people working within call centers. The term became associated with call centers because airlines were among the first large ACD users; the people on the phones were reservation agents.

Analog—A term applied to telephone transmissions where the voice signal is converted into an electrical wave signal that is nearly identical to the sound waves produced by the human voice. Signals in the telephone network are either analog or digital.

Application Generator—Software that produces application software based on a description of the problem or desired solution. These tools permit people without programming skills to produce high-quality application software in relatively short timeframes.

Application Program Interface (API)—A software interface that allows communications between two devices.

Application Service Provider (ASP)—An organization that provides software suites to companies on a usage fee basis usually via VPNs or the Internet. The economic justification for this approach is that the using company does not have to develop or maintain an IT organization or the expertise requisite to support the complex software suite. The ASP business model is usually directed towards providing Enterprise Resource Planning (ERP) software and Customer Relationship Management (CRM) applications.

Area Code Allocation—A process associated with routing "800" calls among multiple contact centers wherein the area code of the caller is used to determine which center will receive the call attempt.

Automated Attendant—A subset of applications found on Interactive Voice Response systems. This application permits organizations to replace human attendants. These systems use prerecorded human voice to prompt callers to self-direct their calls by pressing keys on the telephone keypad, which deliver the caller to a function or a particular person in the organization.

Automatic Call Distributor (ACD)—A computer-controlled voice-switching system that automatically answers incoming calls, determines the nature of the call, directs the call to an answer resource skilled in that kind of transaction and produces operations reports on the efficiency of the call center.

Automatic Number Identification (ANI)—Typically referred to as "Annie," this is a telephone service that provides the telephone number of the party placing an incoming call on an "800" circuit.

Average Speed of Answer (ASA)—One of the earliest metrics associated with handling telephone calls. ASA has slowly lost favor as the top-level metric to service level because averages tend to disguise the queue times that a significant, albeit minority, of callers actually experience.

Basic Rate Interface—A circuit that provides the user with two Bearer (B) channels and one data (D) channel and is referred to as 2B+D. The bandwidth allocation is two 64,000-bits-per-second channels and one 16,000-bits-per-second data channel for signaling.

Call Center—A place where callers can quickly and efficiently conduct transactions with trained, skilled company representatives or obtain needed information from automated sources.

Call Processing—A software routine typically inside an ACD that permits users to define a set of rules that direct incoming calls to the appropriate answer resource.

Caller ID—A telephone service that provides the telephone number of the party placing a call to the called party.

Central Office—A term applied to very large switching systems maintained by the telephone companies that provide service to a designated local area. Central office switches are also referred to as "exchanges."

Centrex—A telephone system usually supplied by the local telephone company. The switching equipment is located in the telephone company central office. The only equipment at the customer premises are the telephones. One of the attractions of Centrex systems is that the system is rented rather than owned.

Circuit Switching—A methodology for moving digital and analog information wherein computer-controlled switching equipment is instructed to set up a continuous connection from the sender to the receiver. This connection remains in place even when no bits are being transmitted. Circuit switching is the technology upon which the existing telephone system is built. It is the opposite of Packet Switching.

Client/Server Architecture—Information technology in which the client (PC or workstation) requests information from a server. Servers may be high-speed micro-, mini- or mainframe computers. The client system provides the user interface and performs some or all of the application processing. The server maintains databases and processes requests from the various clients to extract data from, or to update, the database.

Codec—A word derived from the words "code" and "decode." It refers to a solid-state device that digitizes human analog voice waveforms into bit streams and then back into analog voice waveforms.

Computer Telephony Integration (CTI)—A generic term applied to hardware and software that permits a telephony device, like an ACD or PBX, to communicate with the databases in the enterprise. CTI is an enabling technology that makes possible screen pops and data-directed routing.

Conditional Transaction Routing—A functionality in transaction routing whereby the system can access a set of real-time variables concerning the system, application and agent conditions. These variables are tested and depending upon the outcome of the test, different actions are taken.

Contact Center—A term increasingly being applied to multimedia-enabled call centers. This is an evolved call center that integrates the Internet into its operations. Typically, contact centers include text chat, e-mail handling, Web site support technologies and self-help devices operating in the voice and Web worlds.

Customer Premises Equipment (CPE)—Communications equipment that resides on the customer's premises. This is the opposite of telephony services provided by Centrex.

Data-Directed Routing—The process of routing a caller based on information that exists about that caller within enterprise databases. For example, a contact center might wish to route calls from its best customers to agents ahead of other callers.

Dense Wavelength Division Multiplexing (DWDM)—A fiberoptic technology wherein each individual fiber strand is actually divided into the individual wavelengths of light that make up white light. In this way, each wavelength of light on each strand can carry its own data stream.

Dialed Number Identification Service (DNIS)—An interexchange carrier service offering wherein typically the last four numbers dialed by the calling party are transmitted to the ACD and help identify what kind of transaction the caller requires. DNIS is fundamentally similar to Direct Inward Dialing (DID), a feature commonly found in Private Branch Exchanges (PBX).

Digital—A device that uses binary code to represent information. In the world of telephony, this term refers to encoding of an analog voice waveform into digital values represented by bits. The advantage of digital transmission over analog transmission is greater fidelity and resistance to extraneous noise sources, like lightning and radio frequency interference.

Direct Inward Dialing (DID)—Calls to a DID number are routed directly to that number without the use of an operator and extension numbers.

Dual Tone Multi-Frequency (DTMF)—This is the formal name of touch-tone technology. Each key on the telephone keypad is an acoustic combination of two frequencies.

E1 Line—The European version of a digital circuit that provides 32 voice channels and a signaling channel. The U.S. version is called a T1 line.

E-Mail—An electronic message usually sent from one person to another. The message contains the recipient's address, subject line, message, attachments and signature. Attachments to e-mail messages might consist of data files, programs, audio or video files and links to other web sites.

E-Mail Auto Response—This function involves receiving a customer's e-mail message and providing responses, usually prewritten, based on a software routine's analysis of the message content.

Erlang—A statistician who lived more than 100 years ago who created several statistical tables which, surprisingly, are used today to calculate the number of trunks needed to handle calling demand expressed in hours and the number of agents required to meet a particular service level goal. The two tables most frequently used are Erlang B (used for trunk calculation) and Erlang C (used for agent staffing calculation).

Ethernet—A local area network transmission protocol wherein devices with information to transmit "listen" to the traffic on the network and insert their packets when possible. Devices are sensitive to packet collision and will retransmit packets so affected.

Event Code—Also sometimes referred to as a wrap-up code, this term refers to digits entered by the agent at the conclusion of a telephone call that represents call disposition information.

Facsimile (Fax)—The communication of anything printed on a page between distant locations. Fax machines are able to scan a page and transmit a coded image over telephone lines. The receiving fax machine prints a replica of the original page.

Fax-on-Demand—This is a technology enhancement to an existing system whereby callers can automatically request that information be transmitted to them via fax machines.

Fiberoptic Cable—Thousands of individual glass fibers are arranged into a bundle. These bundles are laid along railroad right-of-ways or inside pipelines and serve as backbones, or high-speed and high-capacity, networks. Fiber networks typically utilize packet-switching technologies. Each fiber strand is capable of handling high-speed data streams.

First-Party CTI—Computer telephony integration application performed entirely upon the agent's desktop. No CTI server is involved. Caller identification information is conveyed to the softphone application running on the agent's PC and automatically pasted into the data access application.

Freephone Service—Telephone service offering wherein the caller is not charged for the call. Rather, the receiving party pays for the call. In the United States, this offering is called "800" or In-Wats service.

Graphical User Interface (GUI)—Referred to as "gooey," this is a graphics-based user interface that employs icons, pull-down menus and mouse clicks on the part of the user to cause the system to function in desired ways. This technique has largely replaced the text-based command line approach used in earlier generations of software.

Hypertext Mark-Up Language (HTML)—A high-level language used to create the look and feel of the content found on Web site pages.

InterExchange Carrier (IXC)—The term applied to telephone companies that provide long distance service. In the United States, the dominant interexchange carriers are AT&T, Worldcom and Sprint.

Integrated Services Digital Network (ISDN)—A service offering involving digital telephone circuits in which the voice bits have been separated from data bits that facilitate network switching and billing functions. ISDN circuits come in two forms—Basic Rate and Primary Rate. For more details, see the glossary definitions for each circuit form.

Interactive Voice Response (IVR)—A software application residing upon a powerful PC that permits a caller to retrieve information from computer databases by listening to voice prompts and responding with telephone keypad depressions. This technology is being revitalized by natural language, speaker-independent, voice recognition.

Internet Protocol (IP)—This protocol is responsible for ensuring that packets are sent to the right destination.

Jitter—In a packet-switching environment, where individual packets can traverse multiple different routes to their destination, this term refers to the frequent occurrence where packets arrive out of order. This imposes either greater delay on the assembly of the entire message or causes the message to have missing pieces, albeit very small. In voice over IP, jitter accounts for lower fidelity.

Latency—This is another way of saying delay. In packet-switching networks, this term refers to the delay imposed by the distance (minimal) and the number of routers (potentially many) the packet traverses to arrive at its destination.

Local Area Network (LAN)—A communication network that provides service to users in a defined area such as a building, LAN consists of servers, workstations, a network operating system and a communications link. The two most prevalent LAN technologies are Ethernet and Token Ring.

Management Information System (MIS)—Software designed to provide real-time and historical reporting of information of interest to management and staff about contact center performance.

M-Commerce—Coined by William Safire, this word represents the world of mobile commerce.

Occupancy—A measure expressed as a percentage of the total sign-in time spent by an agent handling transactions and doing any necessary work related to that transaction. If occupancy is too high for protracted periods of time, the center risks absenteeism, excessive sick leave, turn-over and/or pacing behavior. Acceptable levels of occupancy are entirely dependent upon the size of the agent team. Very large teams can produce acceptable occupancy levels in the low 90 percentile while smaller teams will find acceptable occupancy levels in the mid-80s.

Open System—A term used to describe a manufacturer-independent system. In contact centers, products from other vendors can be easily integrated. In a larger sense, it means that the hardware required to run the application can be purchased from any of a variety of sources which helps ensure lower acquisition costs.

Packet Switching—A methodology for moving digital information wherein small containers carry a discrete number of bits of information. Each packet contains an address representing the packet's destination. Implicit in packet networks is the notion of no central intelligence. Each packet finds its own way to the destination from among thousands–or millions–of possible paths. Packet switching is the opposite of circuit switching.

Percent Allocation—A term used to describe the allocation of "800" calls among multiple contact centers by percentage points. In practice, the service control point would be instructed to send 30% of the calls to Center A, 50% to Center B and 20% to Center C, for example.

Portal—The term applied to a "gateway" to information on the Internet.

Power Dialer—A system that automatically dials numbers from a list, differentiates between system intercept tones, busy signals, answering machines, ring-no-answer and actual human voice to present agents with live contacts.

Predictive Dialer—This is a more sophisticated version of power dialing. The system dials ahead of agent availability and attempts to match the actual answer rate with predictions about when agents will finish their existing conversations.

Primary Rate Interface—A circuit more commonly known in the United States as a T-1 span line, it consists of 24 bearer channels and one data channel. In Europe and other areas of the world, a variation on Primary Rate Interface exists where there are 32 bearer channels and one data channel; it is called an E-1 circuit.

Private Branch Exchange (PBX)—A telephone system that is typically found in most business enterprises. It is connected to the public switch telephone network by trunks, provides connectivity to station users and permits internal conversations between subscribers without using outside networks.

Protocol—These are the rules governing the transmission of data.

Quality of Service (QOS)—This term refers to the increasing realization that while all packets traveling the Internet are equal today, they probably should not be. Some packets are more important than others, like packets containing pieces of voice conversation. If Voice over IP (VoIP) will ever become practical on the World Wide Web, quality of service issues will have to be resolved.

Queue—A waiting list. Callers are frequently placed into a queue awaiting an available agent.

Router—A highly specialized, high-power computer that accepts packets, reads their destination addresses and sends them to the next closest router to their final destination at incredible rates.

Screen Pop—This term describes the capability of an ACD system to communicate with a firm's database through CTI software so that information about the caller appears on the agent's screen at the same moment the caller is connected to that agent.

Script—Agents sometimes use an on-screen script to handle a call. A well-written script that considers all potential branches that a conversation might take can dramatically reduce training time for new agents in the contact center.

Server—A computer in a client/server environment that processes requests from clients.

Service Control Point (SCP)—A high-speed, high-power computer database used by InterExchange Carriers (IXCs) in conjunction with Signaling System 7 to decode the physical telephone number behind "800" numbers.

Service Level—The contact centers metric used that specifies what percentage of call are answered in some number of seconds or less. Typically, contact center service levels may be expressed as 80% in 20 seconds or less.

Spam—A derogatory term applied to unwanted e-mail or e-mail messages mass-mailed to groups or lists of people.

T1 Line—A digital circuit with a bandwidth of 1.544 million bits per second that provides for 24 voice paths and a signaling channel.

Telephony Application Programming Interface (TAPI)—Referred to as "tap-ee," this programming interface from Microsoft and Intel allows Windows client applications to access voice services on a server. It is designed to provide interoperability between PCs and telephone equipment, including phone systems and PBXs.

Telephony Services Application Programming Interface (TSAPI)—Referred to as "t-sap-ee," this telephony programming interface from Novell and AT&T provides interoperability between PCs and telephone equipment. It is designed to interface a telephone PBX with a NetWare server.

Text Chat—A Web site support technology wherein a Web site visitor clicks on a "contact us" button to obtain needed real-time support. The browser window opens a secondary window in which the visitor and a Web-enabled agent can conduct a real-time text chat session.

Third-Party CTI—A computer telephony integration that is facilitated by a server that has access to the ACD system and to enterprise databases. The ACD system sends caller identification information together with the position number of the agent who will get the call. The server can then fetch the caller's data and paint it on the screen simultaneously with the connection of the caller with the agent.

Token Ring—A local area network transmission protocol wherein each device receives a software "token" sequentially permitting that device to transmit a packet of information. The device then passes the token to the next device.

Transmission Control Protocol (TCP)—This software breaks down data files into packets of about 1,500 characters at the origination point and reassembles those packets at the receiving end.

Virtual Contact Centers—Multiple contact centers, located in different geographical areas, function as a single center by using links between the sites or by performing call routing within the network before the calls arrive at the sites.

Virtual Private Network (VPN)—This product offering from carriers gives user organizations more control and security over communications than if they made use of the public network. As the name implies, control and security issues are easier to deal with if an organization does not share the facilities. This service provides the user with the benefits of having a private network without the cost of building one.

Voice Mail—A specialized software application that digitizes incoming human voice messages and stores them on disk. The application allocates the disk into discrete mailboxes and gives the owner the ability to review, store and delete voice messages.

Voice Over IP (VoIP)—The capability of engaging in a voice conversation over the Internet typically through a multimedia equipped personal computer (e.g., a PC equipped with microphone and speakers). The advantage of this technology lies in the ability to provide real-time support to web site visitors on a single phone line. VoIP is also very attractive to contact center users because it could potentially replace the need for free-phone service like "800" calling.

Web Call-Back—A Web site support technology wherein the Web visitor fills out a brief form on the Web site requesting a telephone call-back at a specific number and specific time to receive needed information.

Web Page Push/Collaboration—This technology allows a contact center agent to interact with a Web site visitor in real time by synching the two browsers. This permits the agent to cause new Web pages to appear in the visitor's Web browser while they engage in text chat or VoIP conversations. This is critical functionality for organizations wishing to cross-sell and up-sell on the Web.

Wide Area Network (WAN)—A communications network that spans a larger geographical area than a Local Area Network, such as a campus or remote facilities. Wide Area Networks require the facilities from interexchange or local exchange carriers.

Wireless Application Protocol (WAP)—A subset of Hypertext Mark-Up Language, it is used to translate Web pages to a format more compatible to the small screens found in mobile phones.

Workflow—A term that refers to how a task is performed. Typically, a task is analyzed and broken down into discrete steps. Information needed at that step is identified. Minimalism is key to keep screen clutter at a minimum. Information not germane to the current task is not provided.

Workforce Management—In the contact center this term refers to software systems that accept transaction handling history, generate forecasts for transaction demand, permit acceptable work shifts to be defined, allow agents to establish work shift preferences, and create individual agent work schedules that attempt to meet service level goals with the minimum expenditure of expensive labor.

About the Author

Bill Durr was educated at the University of Illinois where he was granted B.S. degrees in Marketing and Economics and Northwestern University's Graduate School of Business. Bill became involved with computers in 1968, facsimile in 1970, mainframe application programming in 1973, operating systems in 1974 and local area networks in 1978. Then he discovered the world of voice communications.

In 1978 Bill became intrigued with call centers. Since that time he has held a variety of sales, marketing and management roles for several major call center vendors. He has practical experience with ACD systems, voice mail, interactive voice response, work force management software and network routing software.

Together with Dr. Gene Swystun at Call Center Management Associates, Bill provided call center consulting services to a wide variety of companies. As a consultant, he discovered that technology alone seemed incapable of enabling call centers to provide efficient and effective customer support operations.

A frequent speaker at contact center conventions and seminars, Bill provides topics of interest at events in the United States, United Kingdom, Europe, Africa, Australia and China. He supplies articles on various aspects of the call center/contact center industry and authored a book several years ago that focused upon call center management practices published by Advanstar, entitled *Building a World-Class Inbound Call Center*.

Bill currently lives in the Dallas/Fort Worth area and invites you to call him at 817-488-3430 with any questions or comments.